D1412514

ALL LIE IN WAIT

ALL LIE IN WAIT

By William Samelson

Prentice-Hall, Inc., Englewood Cliffs, New Jersey

To the martyrs of tyranny . . .

CONTENTS

PART ONE

Love, Humor, and Hope

It is all written in the
Prophecy of the sages . . .

And it came to pass . . .

And the sages tell us tales of old,
They censure Evil and praise the Good.

And it came to pass . . .

Loki, the foe of the gods,
Had caused the death of Balder,
The god of light and peace . . .

And it came to pass . . .

And it angered Odin, the god of gods,
Whose favorite son was slain.

And it came to pass . . .

Odin sought to avenge Balder's death.
Solemnly, Odin declared Loki's fate,

And he said:

"Tie him to the granite rock forever!
Let venom take his life!"

And breaking loose, the evil Loki
Swore: "My time will come and
Bring the doom of the gods!"

And it came to pass . . .

The Æsir was consumed with
The fire of vengeance and hate,
And there was peace no more . . .

And it came to pass . . .

The sages lament, when Loki
Appeared once again, as he had pledged.
And he was not alone.
At his side was his faithful brood
Of forces from the sinister realm of Hel,
Vowing to aid Loki in the great struggle
Which ensued of Good against Evil . . .

And it came to pass . . .

And the sages weep,
For they lack words
To speak their sorrow.

And the gods do battle
To the bitter end.
Ragnarök . . .

Mr. Markus Minski
187 Lowell Street
Brooklyn, N. Y.
U.S.A.

May 14, 1939

Dear Uncle Mark:

It has been a long time since I last wrote you, but I want you to know that it was not because of negligence that we have been silent. We thought of you very often and talked about you and planned to write. But, somehow, in the rush of the day and the scarcity of time, we have never gotten to it.

We hope that this letter finds you and Aunt Haya and the children in the best of health and that your business is coming along successfully. My shop is bustling with work, and I have had to hire special help and Bela is working most of the day alongside me. The children are fine and so are we. Roman was Bar Mitzvah in January. I think it must have slipped your mind or you would have sent him a card as you have always done on his birthdays and the other children's too. Wilek will be eleven come next month, and Felusia will be seven in August. If you have a chance, write Roman a note. All the children think the world of the U.S.A. and show your letters and stamps to their friends. They are the envy of the neighborhood, and you are admired and revered because you are their "American Uncle."

There is a lot of talk about this man Hitler in Ger-

9

many. He shouts a great deal on the radio, all about taking back "his possessions" in Poland. He says he will do it soon. People have been asking me about it because they know we have relatives in America, and I don't know what to tell them. What do I tell them? Is America going to let Hitler take over? England promises to fight on our side, but who knows? She always looks after her own interest first. It is like a different world across the channel. People here are frightened and hopeful that America will help.

Although we have lots of customers, there is little money coming in because everyone is holding on to cash. But we can't very well refuse to work, constantly hoping that the situation will improve and things will come to normal once more.

Please give our love to the whole family and write soon. Anxiously expecting your reply, with love and best wishes from

Your nephew,
Henry

Pan Henry Simon
Madrzejowska 3
Sosnowiec, Poland

June 12, 1939

Dear Nephew:
   Your last letter came on Friday, a week ago, and I didn't have a chance to reply sooner because Haya just yesterday returned from the hospital where she was con-

fined since the seventh of May for gall bladder treatment. She has suffered enough. Now she feels better, thank God, and we hope there will be no further complications. She is recovering rapidly, and we hope to have her completely on her feet soon, the Lord willing, blessed be He.

I am sorry to have forgotten Roman's Bar Mitzvah, but you can imagine, what with all the excitement going on here it is easy to forget. I want to take this opportunity to wish him all the best and convey my congratulations. I am sure he will be the source of much nachas to the whole family. Please buy him a gift from us for the enclosed $5.00.

We get many notices about the trouble in Europe, but the sentiment here is that Hitler is only blowing off a little steam to show his people that he means well with them. Every dictator needs a scapegoat, and he is like all the others. But he'll think twice before he attacks anyone because this country won't stand for it. We will fight on the side of our Allies, of course. Even here in New York the Bund movement is growing day by day. The brown-shirts are marching through the streets in sympathy for their Vaterland, but such are the wondrous ways of democracy. Our people are not idle either, and there are daily street fights between our youth groups and the Bund. This contributes a lot to my worry because Isaac has gotten it into his stubborn head that he should be everywhere there is a ruckus. And little David is quite keen on it too. I don't know what I should do about it anymore.

I am sorry to see that you are passing through a crisis, but as you can see, we don't lack excitement here either. I pray to God that all things will come to normal soon. And don't worry about this fellow Hitler. There are six million Jews in the U. S. and we won't let him harm our brethren.

Give my love to Bela and the children. Haya and the boys send their love.

Your uncle,
Mark

Mr. Markus Minski
187 Lowell Street
Brooklyn, N. Y.
U.S.A.

June 17, 1939

Dear Uncle Mark:

God bless you for your quick reply to my letter of May 14. We are all happy and relieved to hear about Aunt Haya's convalescence. But we all share your worry about Isaac's participation in street fights, although they are not ordinary brawls and the boy follows a noble impulse. He may get hurt, just the same. It pains us to know that one of our very own might get hurt. Explain to him that this is a thing of the law and he should let the police do their duty.

Roman was thrilled that you remembered him in your letter, and he thanks you for the generous gift you enclosed. It was more than ample and you really didn't have to do it. But we thank you just the same.

Dear Uncle, I want you to know that things are happening here rapidly despite all the assurances of the Allies. Hitler is making rapid progress. His agents are *provoking border incidents which he claims are the fault of our people. Only last week he called in an international commission from Geneva for an "on-the-spot" check of the situation and, believe me, he even got them convinced that the dead men in German border-patrol uniforms were slain by the "aggressive" Poles. This incident happened not far from where we live, and I can tell you it was too close for comfort.*

I don't want to make this letter too long, so I will come straight to the point. There are increasing numbers of Jews leaving this country daily as fast as they can procure visas. Most of them would like to go to the United States, but few are fortunate enough to have relatives there. So, they flee to Australia, Brazil, and Argentina. Some travel to countries we have never heard of. They flee for their lives. The danger of the Swastika approaches menacingly.

We would also like to escape the oncoming holocaust. But in order to get a visa to the United States we must have a sponsor, if possible, a relative, who will make out an Affidavit of Support. If you could do this for us, we would be eternally grateful to you, Uncle Mark, and we would repay you in time. Please see what you can do to help us get out of this boiling pot. You are the only one we can turn to, so please don't let us down. Time is of the essence, so hurry!

Give our love to Aunt Haya and the boys. Bela and the children send you their love. Hoping to hear from you soon, I remain as always

> *Your nephew,*
> *Henry*

Pan Henry Simon
Madrzejowska 3
Sosnowiec, Poland

August 3, 1939

Dear Nephew:

One month has gone by, and I've tried to see my way through this thing and I can't. So I must write you to tell you that there is very little we can do for you at this time. My heart cries out to all of you. I am especially anxious for the children, but I am not in the position to bring you here and offer you support. Money does not grow on trees here in the U.S., contrary to the beliefs of all our brethren on your side of the ocean. We work very hard for what we earn, and in the long run have very little to show. Right now I am concerned about so many things at home that I can't see my way clear in committing myself to more responsibilities. The hospital bill for Haya took what reserves we had in money. Perhaps if you'd write to the relief organizations or speak to their representatives there, they would find a way to help you.

I am very sorry, but it has to be this way. I have thought this out and talked it over with Haya, and she sees it the same way I do.

I know you are anxious to hear from me, so I won't delay this any further. Give our love to your wife and the children.

Affectionately,
Your Uncle Mark

Mr. Markus Minski
187 Lowell Street
Brooklyn, N. Y.
U.S.A.

August 20, 1939

Dear Uncle Mark:

I have just returned from the relief organization's office. There were hundreds of people in line. When I finally got to my interviewer, I was told that things cost money and that there are thousands of families throughout Europe as desperate as I, and each one had to wait its turn. Of course, they said, if we had a few hundred dollars, things would go much faster. It seems that dollars are the only acceptable currency in Europe nowadays. Well, when I told the interviewer that I came without money, he very politely led me out of his office and advised me to return when I had something more concrete to offer.

Where should I get the money? I am desperate for the children's sake and for myself and Bela. It would cost about thirteen hundred dollars to get papers for Australia for all of us on the black market. I have a good contact and am quite sure the man is reliable. Please help us before it's too late, Uncle Mark. If there was ever cause for action, it is here now. Much depends upon your promptness. I can promise you that I will repay you as soon as I can. And I want you to know that it never occurred to me that you find money on the streets in the United States of America; I know how hard you work for a living.

Now I hate to burden you with our troubles, but our

15

*lives are in your hands. May God help you to find a way
to aid us. Please remember, I am your brother's only son.
Much love from all of us to all of you.*

Your nephew,
Henry

Pan Henry Simon
Madrzejowska 3
Sosnowiec, Poland

August 30, 1939

My dear Nephew:
*The wings of urgency must have caused your last
letter to arrive here so soon, and I must reply right away
to let you know what we shall do in your behalf. Although I still don't swallow the pessimism of all the
alarmists, and I don't think the Nazis will dare take steps
against Poland, I'll follow your pleas and do all in my
power to help you and your family come to the U.S.
True, we are crowded here and can't offer you the best
conveniences, but we'll try our best. I've already told
Isaac to pick up immigration papers, and I made out a
notarized Affidavit of Support on my way from the
shop tonight. Tomorrow, the first thing in the morning,
we'll send all papers to Washington. It shouldn't take long
for it all to reach our embassy in Warsaw. God willing,
you'll be on your way in no time at all. It is a great pity
for you to have to leave all your possessions there, all you
have worked for and earned. You will come here to an
unknown future to make a new start. But I am beginning
to understand your fears. I only hope that all your anxie-*

16

ties are completely unfounded, for I should never forgive myself for my initial hesitation. May the Almighty help us realize all our desires and unite us soon. I hope and pray that this letter should find all of you in the best of health, as we are all well. Aunt Haya has completely recovered her strength now, thanks to our Maker, blessed be He.

Give my love to all. Kisses for the children.

Your Uncle Mark

✺

The mailman took special pains to deliver the envelope personally. It was Saturday and the Minskis would be home. There were too many seals on it, and he could not make out what they said, but he knew the letter had been returned from Poland, and he made sure it got into the hands of the sender.

Uncle Mark stood in the doorway examining the letter for a while. He could make out the German words with the aid of his knowledge of Yiddish.

"Who is it, Markus?" Haya's voice came from the kitchen and startled him. He extended the arm which held the letter toward his wife.

"It got there too late, Haya. May God help them," he said and handed her the envelope.

✦ THE TURNING POINT

Israel was holy to the Lord,
  the first fruits of his harvest.
All who ate of it became guilty;
  evil came upon them, saith the Lord.
JEREMIAH 2:3

"Where can we go?" Father kept repeating. "I did just what Markus suggested in his last letter and they practically threw me out of the B.I.A.S. How could they treat me like that!"

"Hush, Henry, the children."

"It's better they should know it now, Bela. The truth is we have nowhere to go. Every door in Europe is shut in our faces! It's almost the end of August, and we're still here!"

"Perhaps we should go to Piotrkow for the time being," Mother suggested tentatively. "It's away from the border and chances are the Germans will never come that far."

". . . I can't go with you," Father interrupted. "I've got to report to the Officer's Reserve tomorrow at three o'clock . . . I knew it would come to this."

"We'll send the children ahead and I'll stay with you."

"No Bela, you go with them. The war can't last forever."

There was silence.

"As you say, my dear, whatever you say."

Suddenly Father left the room. We heard him clear his throat as he closed the bathroom door. Then we heard water running. When he came back, he motioned for me to come close to him.

"Wilek, you are old enough now for an important errand. You have had errands before but this one will be unlike the others."

It was the first time Father had made me his confidant and I was frightened. His voice trembled as he continued.

"It is best we move further into the interior. You and Felusia will go immediately to your grandparents in Piotrkow. After a day or two, Mother will follow with Roman. She needs to settle a few things here. When all is done, I shall come too. . . .

"Tomorrow there is a train leaving from Katowice. It would be a great relief to know that you are on it. Mother will go with you as far as Katowice, and you can board the train to Piotrkow there. From there you will be on your own. . . . God be with you."

On September 1, early in the afternoon, the German bombers flew over Piotrkow. The sirens blew but the bombardment had already started and they only added to the confusion. People ran into the street. Children cried and men cursed.

The raid lasted a good ten minutes and the military barracks lay in ruins. Most people had not had time to get to their shelters. Glad to be alive, they marched wearily back to their homes.

A large cloud of smoke came from the east side of town near the arsenal. We could hear the bells of the volunteer fire department and people shouting, "The town is on fire!" I saw several policemen leading a handcuffed man in priest's clothing across the street, and I tugged on Grandfather's arm.

"A genuine spy! Grandfather, they caught a spy!"

"I knew there was something rotten about this sudden bombardment," he said. "He had his hand in it, I tell you." Then he went on telling us about the spies during World War I, but I watched the hunched man in black and wondered whether they would shoot him blindfolded or not. I knew from spy movies that he had a choice.

"How will he die, Grandfather? Will he be given a trial?"

"What is the difference how. One thing is certain, he is a dead man."

Grandfather was in a melancholy mood and for those few moments we forgot our differences. In the total silence, a bond was tied.

The morning following the bombardment, the Council of Elders called a meeting. The patriarchs of the Jewish community gathered to decide what action should be taken in case of another attack.

We heard that men were at work in the arsenal when it got bombed. They were all killed, the first war fatalities in Piotrkow.

"Anyone we know?" someone inquired.

"No, just a few goyim," a voice replied.

"Oh, well, that is different."

Bliższe ciało niż koszula, says an old Polish proverb, one's own skin is closer to one's self than his shirt.

The Council agreed unanimously "There is no place in town like the mikvah for strong walls!"

The mikvah was the ritual bathhouse. It had massive stone walls and sufficient supplies of water. There was only the problem of accommodations. While the mikvah would hold approximately two hundred people, there were about one hundred and fifty Jewish families in Piotrkow. This meant nearly six hundred men, women, and children. Felix

Rabinowicz, a recent arrival from Russia, suggested a solution. "We shall have to draw lots for the mikvah."

"Well said. Well said." The group voiced its approbation.

"Spoken like a true haham. Hear. Hear."

The lots were drawn on the same day and shelter was also provided for those who were not fortunate enough to draw the mikvah.

"Anyway, who is to say which is the more fortunate? Who can guess where the bombs will fall? The Almighty One, blessed be He, holds men's fate in His power," Moshe Lubianski mused philosophically, but he was glad that his family would move to the mikvah.

Grandfather arrived home with mixed emotions. He told Grandmother to start packing all our belongings.

"I have drawn a lot for the mikvah and that is where you must move tonight, you and the children."

"You are not going with us, Grandfather?"

"Come what may, I wish to remain here, even to my dying days."

Grandmother quarreled as usual with her husband for a while, but to no avail. Unfortunately, my grandparents had never learned to discuss issues. Grandmother wept and neighbors listened as Grandfather stamped his feet obstinately. Time was running short and Grandmother finally gave in with a few words of warning.

"Remember to run down to the cellar when the raid comes."

"I shall die in my own bed," was Grandfather's reply.

We gathered a few essentials and a lot of bedding.

Suddenly we heard airplanes and moments later the house shook. We ran down to the cellar as quickly as we could. Also Grandfather stumbled down several steps at a time. As the sound of the explosions approached our section of town, we waited, praying for the planes to leave. No one felt secure. The old castle was close by, with antiaircraft guns on its roof to attract the raiders. We prayed for a miracle, and as though in answer the silence came.

But there had been an hour of continual bombing and a great deal of damage was done. I ran out of the house before anyone could call after me. Scattered groups of people appeared on the street. Some sought new shelter, others looked for their kin. The surprise attack had caught many unaware. Rumor had it that it was the work of the newest and fastest fighter-bombers, the Stukas. There were dead everywhere. Men, women, and children. They were all dead. Many buildings were on fire, many were already smouldering ruins.

Grandfather remained in the house. He insisted. We covered our heads with pillows and walked very quickly, trying not to see. Grandmother prayed. Felusia cried. I said a few prayers myself, those I could remember from the kheder. Bodies were strewn all around. On the sidewalk to our left lay a woman clutching two infants. They were burned to coal.

We entered the mikvah just in time before the Stukas returned for another raid. They struck with sudden force. The ticking of the antiaircraft guns mixed with the detonations of the exploding bombs and the ground trembled again and again.

"What will happen to the dead, Grandmother?"

"They will turn into shadows and serve as a shield to guard us from our enemies."

"Will they?"

"They will."

There were no windows in the mikvah so we searched for a place in candlelight. All kinds of people were there: Jews, Christians, Gypsies, and even one Chinese family, Min Lee, the grocer. Even though they had not drawn lots, they were not turned out. It was a crisis and the mikvah was filled

23

with pity and compassion—filled to the last corner, and we arrived just in time to find a vacant spot near the spiral wrought iron steps leading to the ritual pool.

Grandmother bedded us down but we could not sleep. The walls shook and everyone prayed. Some aloud, others in silence. Polish, Hebrew, Yiddish, and still other languages understood only by God.

Each of the worshipers expressed remorse about one thing or another. Their assurances went toward heaven with each prayer. I listened amazed.

"Why did they do all these evil things and then ask forgiveness?" I whispered.

"I do not really know, my dear."

The bombardment went on for fourteen days, and every moment seemed longer for the incertitude of it. The sound and tremor of the exploding bombs and artillery missiles were soothed only by the persistent prayer of our people. When the holocaust was interrupted at last, it seemed as though all life had ceased. People speculated on the significance of the sudden silence: optimists believed it indicated a repulsion of the enemy; pessimists were sure the invader was gathering his forces for a final blow.

Suddenly we heard insistent knocking on the massive mikvah door, but no one dared step forward and ask who it was. The ground trembled again. The Stukas were rapidly approaching and explosions resounded anew.

"Let us inside, for God's sake, let us in."

I was certain I recognized a voice but crouched against the wall immobile with fear.

"Grandmother, please open the door. Tell someone quickly, those are our friends."

"How can you be certain. It could be anyone out there. We must leave things the way they are."

"But I recognized the voice. It's Nora, the girl that helped us on the train. Grandmother, please."

Shlomo Ganev, the grocer, with a prayer on his lips, unbolted the door and let the desperate group inside. It was Nora, her uncle Max Mandel, and his son Hayim.

"Hear O Israel, the Lord our God, the Lord is one," the people prayed.

I ran to Nora and she touched my cheek. While her uncle was busy talking to the men, I led Nora to Grandmother, who thanked her for all she had done for us on the train and asked her to share our corner in the mikvah. Nora nodded and I was glad.

Max Mandel had come to the mikvah in search of a minyan for his son's Bar Mitzvah. Today Hayim was to enter adult life in accordance with the age-old Jewish ritual, and Max had been unable to gather ten adult Jews in their previous hiding place, the predominantly gentile section on Ulica Marszalkowska. They decided to take advantage of the bombing pause to run over to the mikvah and satisfy tradition.

Descending the narrow steps to the ritual baths, I observed the preparations for the Bar Mitzvah of Hayim Mandel. A makeshift altar, two suitcases covered with a tallis, was erected in the middle of the hall. Candles were lit and placed on both sides and the men wearing their tallisim assembled, their bowed figures reflecting sinister shadows on the wall. The procedures seemed solemn and frightening. Hayim was hesitant and I was glad not to be in his place.

The women formed the outer circle of the worshipers. In accordance with the Law, they could not be part of the minyan. The ceremony commenced. Isaac the Gabah led the congregation in prayer with all the dignity of his position.

"*Borchu es Adonai hamvorah, Baruch Adonai hamvorach leolam vaed* . . ."

"I now accept my faith and the faith of my fathers

with all the privileges and the responsibilities attached thereto . . ."

For the first time Hayim put on the sacred phylacteries; the t'filin. He placed one on his forehead and the other on the pit of his elbow. The small cubes contained excerpts from the Torah and were to be worn thereafter each time he worshiped. They belonged to the past, yet they were to become the strength of the present. Men swayed to the rhythmic Hasidic chants and clapped their hands. The chanting and the clapping and the bombing continued.

"Mazal tov, mazal tov."

The Bar Mitzvah ceremony lasted over two hours and the ground still trembled. But, the initially frightening effect of the renewed explosions had lessened by now and the Bar Mitzvah uplifted everyone. We scarcely realized, for those two hours, that it was already the third week we had been in hiding.

The services ended and the participants joined their families. Felix joined us. "Just for a while," he said. He seemed pensive and depressed.

"Were you ever Bar Mitzvah?" I asked.

"I was. Father insisted. It is all such utter nonsense. No one matures through ceremony. Man must face reality; only then can he claim his right to existence, only then, you hear!"

Several explosions caused the outburst to quickly terminate. Felix retired to the wall opposite ours. I could see him muttering to himself. He was the typical man in the middle; hated by those who did not understand him, feared by those who did, and persecuted by both.

It was a dark but unquiet night. We lay still, Nora and I, arm in arm and body to body, saying nothing. It was a pure innocent closeness. The earth shook often.

And it came to pass . . .

Odin sat, listening to the Sybil's chant,
She spoke of chaos, and the world before
Gods came to be, before there was
Love and Faith, before deliberate destruction . . .

And the sages also lent their ears . . .

৵ৡৡ THE INVADERS

And their houses shall be turned
unto others,
Their fields and their wives
together;
For I will stretch out my hand
upon the inhabitants of the land,
Saith the Lord.
JEREMIAH 6:12

The bombardment subsided early one morning. We waited. Everyone expected a resumption. Candles were lit. Prayers were said. Anxiety was reflected on the faces of all present.

"What now?" someone asked.

"We must be patient."

"We must wait."

"Wait? For what?"

"Who knows? Just wait. Time will tell."

"A learned Rabbi once said that there is perhaps one cardinal sin: *impatience*. Because of that we were driven out of Paradise and for the same reason we cannot return."

We waited. The elders assembled once again, deliberating seriously. Waiting was becoming part of our existence. The second day came, and still silence.

"Why not get out again and survey the situation?"

"Why not? After all, we have done it before."

"Who will go?"

The men looked at one another. Families clustered together, seeking security in closeness. I ran for the door, and moments later breathed the air of the defeated town.

In many places, all that remained were chimneys. Now and then an entire wall was miraculously left. Plumbing pipes wound their way to former bathrooms and kitchens. Solitary sinks hung in mid air.

Here and there a detachment of the once proud Polish Army units, now Kriegsgefangene, were stripped of their insignia, guarded by invaders, and observed by their countrymen. Apologetic looking young warriors. There were no songs. Bare feet and empty stomachs. And only a few weeks earlier we were told that our armed forces were well prepared, well-nigh invincible.

The thumping of invader boots upon the pavement. It would be painful for all those in the mikvah to face.

Children boldly followed the invaders and pleaded for scarce items. They seemed kind, the Wehrmacht men, and from time to time tossed an unusual-looking German coin. As it fell on the pavement, the children scrambled for the "charity." There was no reward for the weak.

The results of the Blitzkrieg were most acutely felt by the homeless. They wandered looking for shelter and salvaging whatever buried property the debris would yield. Some sat in the rubble of their homes, unable to mourn.

Basically, the town was tranquil. The silence of smouldering ruins was only occasionally disturbed by an outcry.

I walked toward the public square where the "bomb shelters" were dug only a few weeks ago. There were crowds, but the trenches were level with the ground.

"Any victims?" someone inquired.

"All dead. Buried alive."

"But they said there was safety in the shelters."

Digging parties attempted to make their way into the trenches at one end where there used to be an entrance.

One of the German garrisons had established its quarters in the ancient castle only one block from Zamkowa 20. There was a shortage of food, and articles such as bread and potatoes were sold on the black market to whoever could afford them. We could not. Grandfather continued to toy with the rubles in his attic. Grandmother was as thrifty as ever, holding onto her meager savings. To top it all, we were expecting Mother and Roman to arrive in Piotrkow any day. My grandparents complained about their arrival and the added hardships it would cause. Something had to be done quickly.

The guard smiled when I approached the gate of the castle. I raised my right hand high into the air in a salute.

"Heil Hitler!"

"Heil Hitler!" was the reply.

We learned fast.

"Bist du Deutscher?" The guard associated everyone who spoke the Führer's language with his Vaterland.

"My father is German. Oberschlesier. My mother is half German and half Polish."

"Ach, Volksdeutscher!" The guard's attitude was friendly and I was happy that he did not inquire into Father's whereabouts.

"Is there anything I could do here to earn a little food?" I asked.

"Ja, there must be something for our landspeople. You must not starve. After all, we are fighting for *you*, aren't we? Tell me, what's your name?" the guard asked.

"Wilek . . . but really it is Wilhelm; they call me Wilek for short."

"Well, we will call you Wilhelm here. And if we want it shorter, it will be Willi. Good?"

"All I want is work."

"Hey, da," the guard called out to a passer-by, a tall, rather stout soldier. "Take this young fellow to the Unteroffizier. He is looking for a job. Er ist Deutscher. Geh' mit ihm, Wilhelm, das ist Hans Müller, der wird dich zum Unteroffizier leiten." I remembered the greeting once again:

"Heil Hitler!"

"Heil Hitler! Komm' mit," Müller reacted brusquely.

We walked through the arched corridors of the ancient castle. Through the ages, those ancient walls have housed many invaders. Each had devastated the fertile valleys of Poland, trampled the fields and cities; most were driven back. The old castle walls housed the victor and the vanquished indiscriminately.

My host knocked respectfully at a door marked "Unteroffizier Boost." "Herein!" We were told to enter. Inside, Boost sat comfortably in an old reclining chair, a pipe between his nicotine-stained teeth, reading a newspaper.

"Was haben wir hier?" he inquired with a friendly smile.

"Heil Hitler! Herr Unteroffizier Boost, ich melde gehorsam, young Wilhelm here, wishes to work for us." Müller stood at attention.

Boost stood up reluctantly. He responded to Müller's "Heil" with a customary military greeting.

"Danke, Müller, that will be all."

Müller snapped another "heil" at his superior. He made an impeccable about-face and left the room.

Boost was a tall, skinny man. He wore his uniform well, he was neat, but not overly meticulous.

"You will shine our boots, wash dishes, and clean up the place in the evenings. Can you do all this? Can you be our Hausbursche? You know, that can be a big job for a little fellow like you!" His concern seemed genuine.

"Yes, I know, Herr Unteroffizier, but I want to earn for the family."

31

"Very well," Boost said, "come with me and I'll explain your duties."

He went on ahead and I followed. We entered the room which he occupied with seven enlisted men. They were all part of the food-storage and transportation detachment, the Verpflegungskompanie, an impressive long name for a simple task. Boost was the Unteroffizier in charge of his platoon. The men were eating when we entered. The first to see Boost yelled "Achtung!" and the men jumped to their feet, arms stretched out toward the ceiling with a brisk, "heil Hitler!"

"Weiter-machen, carry on. Relax. I only wanted to introduce Willi to you. I hope that he might lighten our burdens of this campaign. Willi is our new Hausbursche."

There was a murmur of satisfaction and I was glad to have been welcomed by the invaders. I could go home to tell my grandparents not to worry about the arrival of the rest of the family.

As we were leaving the premises Boost pointed to an inscription on one of the walls: LA GUERRE ET UN GRAND MALHEUR. And then, more to himself than to me, he murmured, "The war is a terrible misfortune for *all*, the victors as well as the vanquished."

When I left him that day, he casually mentioned that as time went on I would become acquainted with the rest of his men. He was apologetic for not having introduced me to all on that day.

There were many like Hans Boost. He was a good-natured man from Leipzig in Saxony and scarcely knew what it was that had brought him to Poland. His wife managed the small hardware store for him and his two little girls attended school. They were told their father was at war to defend the Vaterland.

Hans had never gone farther than the sixth grade. Now he was away from home. They had told him one day to appear, mit saubrer Unterkleidung (with clean underwear), at ten o'clock in the morning on Friedrichstrasse 10, the regimental headquarters. He did what he was told to do. He was a simple man.

There was one in that room, however, who believed. His name was Karl Fritzke. Blond and blue-eyed, he was a member of the NSDAP and proud of it. Because the others felt he had been planted among them, they kept quiet when he was around.

Karl came from Borna, a small town in Saxony. He was the son of an industrial worker, unemployed since World War I. From his early youth, he learned to hate the Treaty of Versailles, the wealthy. When Karl had reached his fifteenth birthday, the black mustache came to power in Germany. Karl joined the Hitler-Jugend program, because it was fun and because he was given a fancy uniform with a swastika on his left sleeve. He liked the rallies at midnight with the flaming torches and he liked to march to the sounds of the powerful brass bands. Karl Fritzke was thankful for the new job the Führer gave his father in the reactivated munitions factory.

Karl had never before hated Jews. But he learned to hate this prime "enemy" of his fatherland as he hated the Treaty of Versailles. Although Karl himself did not put the torches to the houses of worship, he stood by. And when his troops ransacked Jewish homes, he took what was rightfully his as proclaimed by the black mustache . . .

When I returned home that afternoon, elated over my new job, I discovered that there was double cause for celebration. My grandparents, so seldom happy, announced that we had received news about the arrival of Mother and Roman.

They arrived the next day on the 1:25 P.M. from Czestochowa—the train which had brought Felusia and me to Piotrkow. And it was the same station where we had gotten off. But things had changed already. The grotesque web-like steel dome above our heads had been bent by the heat of the fire. Most painfully we felt the absence of the voices. The faces of the best of our nation. And in their place were the invaders.

❧

And it came to pass . . .

The sages mourn the coming of
Loki and his accursed mercenaries.

And the gods engaged in mortal combat,
The Æsir resounded with thunder and lightning,
And the earth shook fearfully
In its foundations . . .

◈ THE GHETTO

*The sword is without, and the pestilence
and famine within;
He that is in the field shall die with
the sword, and he that is in the city,
famine and pestilence shall devour him.*
EZEKIEL 7:15

Early one morning on my way to work in the castle, I
saw a group of people gathered in front of Shlomo's grocery
store. The grocer had donated a board upon which notices
were customarily put up by the military governors for immediate public attention. It was an official notice, and bore the
stamp of the Third Reich and the Seventh Bureau; a fierce
black eagle clutching the swastika.

BEKANNTMACHUNG

NACH DEM WILLEN DES FÜHRERS UND AUF
AUFTRAG DES GAULEITERS WERDEN ALLE JUDEN
VOM JUNI 1940 EIN ARMBAND MIT JUDENSTERN
AM LINKEN ARM ZU TRAGEN VERANLASST . . .

"What goes on here?" I asked Isaac the Gabah.
"Something new for us, a star," he replied with concern.
"What of it?"
"You can be sure it's nothing g . . ." He caught his
tongue in time. People were becoming aware of the newly
created breed of informers in their midst. They began to feel
the effects of the new regime even in their own homes.

35

"A star, the mark of Cain."

"The streets of Piotrkow will resemble Hollywood from now on," someone said jokingly, "you'll see stars everywhere."

Another change. We had experienced many changes; none for the better. The enemy police showed unending vigor and ingenuity in their planned elimination of the Jew. They called it the "strategy of decimation," or Judenreinigung.

The activities of the Seventh Bureau began with a systematic elimination of the intelligentsia. Most of these were rounded up during the night. Then, the Judenrat was established. It consisted of fourteen wealthy Jews—the only ones who could pay for the coveted positions of agents in the administration of the Nazi Kultur program.

Grandfather was approached by Popiawski, the grocer called Shlomo Ganev, to contribute to the "cause" and become one of the members of the Judenrat.

"I should have lived this long only to discover that I don't know my lifelong friends?" said Grandfather with reproach.

"What do you mean by that, Srulko?" Shlomo paused. "Aren't you the first one to whom I make this offer? I could have gone to many before you; there are many takers, you know. Warszawski himself sent me to you. The whole community holds you in great esteem, Srulko, you must know that." He used his arguments well. "We need you, Srulko. The people like you. You are known and respected everywhere. You *must* join the Judenrat."

"So this is where the dog is buried. You want to use me in dealing with our people. You knew all along that they might be suspicious of your activities! You would like to use my honesty to cover up the filth of your politics! Out of my house! Get out this very moment!"

"Think of your children, Srulko, think of your grandchildren," Shlomo faintly attempted to contradict. He did not mention that members of the Judenrat were appointed by the police authority; or that their chief task was to supply Jews for labor detachments from which they themselves were exempt.

"You go on thinking of your family any way you know how, and I will think about the welfare of mine the best way I can." Grandfather tried to compose himself. "As for the offer you have made me, I am honored but I cannot see myself as an official. I have seen too many officials who are all official and no heart. And in my humble opinion, the most despicable character of a man is an official without a heart, for he will commit murder in the name of his office. I have no desire to join the swelling ranks of parasitic officialdom."

"I can understand your desire to stay away from the Judenrat because you have little, if any, faith in its function. But I want you to know that each day there are more refugees from the west, especially from Germany. They arrive on every train. They push themselves into every avenue of our life. They are gaining influence because they know the language of the invader. They know him."

"If they knew the invader as well as you imply, then why are they here? Why aren't they in their own homes?" Srulko insisted. "Anyway, somehow I can't see the connection between your original purpose and the things you try to bring up at this time," he added abruptly.

"I'll tell you the reasons. I'll show you the importance of my mission here," Shlomo said in his trembling voice. "The German Jew arrived in our community not with thanks and appreciation for the helping hand we extended to him in need. On the contrary, he came to us filled with an air of superiority. He has forgotten his Jewishness in his state of assimilation and, for the most part, he blames us, yes Srulko, he holds you and me responsible for the events leading up to his persecution by the Nazi regime. I wouldn't be surprised if he believes the Nazi fabrication about the Jewish conspiracy to rule the world. But he thinks that we were the ones to conspire because he is certain it was not his desire to rule the world. It is obvious that he is more German than Jew, so of course he will attempt to prove his loyalties to his countrymen. Are you willing to stand by while he demonstrates his loyalty at the expense of our families?" Shlomo caught his breath; it was evident that he was truly concerned.

Grandfather insisted once again that he was not interested in the sentiments of the German Jews. He refused to worry about a few Yekes, as the Polish Jews called their German brethren.

"What, then, are you concerned with, Srulko?"

"I am worried about my self-respect. Furthermore, I am not ready to pay with someone else's misery for my temporary safety. When the good Lord wishes to punish me, He will do so without the permission of the Judenrat, I am sure, may His name be blessed."

As may have been expected, Shlomo departed a defeated man. It was not because Srulko refused to join the native mercenary force of hirelings and informers, but because from then on there was an end to all illusions. Shlomo knew all along of the Bureau's simple prison psychology: organize the Jew to sell out his brethren. Yet, he could not help rationalizing his actions in order to continue. No one quit the Gestapo without repercussions. Were it not for his attachment to life, Shlomo might have turned honest.

Although our freedom of movement was becoming more restricted, I kept my job as an orderly for the Supply Company. Each day as I approached the old castle, I tucked the identification band under my shirt. Though I realized full well that my tactics endangered Boost's life, I did not have the courage to tell him I was a Jew. The way things were, Boost would not remain in Piotrkow much longer. Lithuanian troops in black SS uniforms arrived in large numbers. They served as sentries during curfew hours, a task for which the Wehrmacht had been employed until then. There were rumors that the British were defeated at Dunkirk, and that the Nazis had occupied Denmark, Belgium, and France. France had fallen! That was the most difficult rumor to accept. France and England had promised to help us. With their aid, we were to drive the enemy out of our country and march on to Berlin!

One of my duties as orderly was that of an interpreter. Frequently Boost and I went to the market together to shop. Here and there a farmer would become suspicious of my knowledge of German; he would point at me and utter the only coherent German word he knew, "Jude." I suspected Boost knew all along, but he dismissed the denunciation with a sly smile and a shrug of his shoulders.

Christmas of 1940 had come, and with it another major speech of the Führer. I sat in the arched room of the medieval castle and listened for almost three hours to the incoherent shouts of the black mustache. It was not too difficult to understand why his followers became carried away. He spoke with a pathological frenzy that gripped millions of his followers with a maniacal fury.

A murmur went through the room when the Führer concluded with the familiar phrase, "Nächste Weihnachten sind wir zu Hause!" Next Christmas his troops would be home with their loved ones. "Deutschland, Deutschland über alles, über alles in der Welt . . . Sieg! Heil!"

Meanwhile, the town grew in population. Most of the newcomers were of German-Jewish origin, but Western European Jews also kept arriving steadily. Living conditions became intolerably congested. Worst of all was the incompatibility of the newly acquired "tenants" with the people and the environment they were to call their own for some time to come.

The Judenrat kept a rigid census, and the new arrivals

registered all pertinent data—health, age, and financial situation—at the Militia office before being assigned to their new quarters. Almost all of the refugees were left without means due to the thoroughness of the Gestapo confiscation specialists.

When Grandfather heard that refugees might be assigned to our house he shouted at the top of his voice. "They are not going to deposit one of these German convert families in my house."

"Now, Srulko, these are poor, homeless people," Grandmother said softly. "They need shelter, and we have some room for them, so why not let a good family from among these defeated people live with us?"

"A good family? Did you say a good family?" Srulko waved his arms. "There aren't any good families among converts; they are worse than the goyim proper!"

He considered the Reform German Jew a convert and was not alone in his diagnosis. Most of the Polish Jewry was orthodox, and all of the Jews in Piotrkow were ultra-orthodox. To them any Jew who was less than a Hasid must have been a shmadnik, a convert. Moreover, the Hasid, because he was obvious in his appearance, became the first target of the SS and the Hitler Youth who roamed through the shtetl streets in search of victims. Beards were cut with dull-edged bayonets and beatings were common daily occurrences. The Hasid felt that he suffered for the transgressions of the intruders, the converts.

"If you think that I will turn the other cheek, you're mistaken. We'll see about that! No shmadnik is going to share my home!" With that exclamation Grandfather left the apartment hastily.

Grandfather's second cousin on his mother's side, Moritz Lazar, was a man of considerable influence at SS headquarters. He made custom-fitted boots for the Sturmbannführer and the Obersturmbannführer, and his dealings extended as far up the ladder of the ruling hierarchy as the all-powerful Brigadeführer. Higher than that the modest aspirations of a humble shoemaker did not venture to soar. With each higher rank of boots he made, Uncle Moritz acquired a greater degree of influence. At one time he was possibly the most influential Jew in Piotrkow, with influence extending further than all the money of the Judenrat put together. Money had a finite quality about it, but Uncle Moritz's inherent ability would last as long as his talent was needed by his demanding masters; the special boot-hide and leather would be provided by his satisfied clients when his supply ran out.

Who else but Uncle Moritz could help allocate the Mandels to our house? He could effect the move "legally," and then there would be no question about accepting a family of shmadniks. Uncle Moritz thought Grandfather's request a bit trivial, but it was important to Srulko, and he was his second cousin, although ten years his senior, on his mother's side. He could not refuse.

"All right, all right," he interrupted Grandfather's shouting. "I'll see what can be done about it."

"Look at him! The big makher! The big shot! He'll see what can be done!" Grandfather shouted again. "You sound more like your employers each day! You even wear their kind of boots! Why, you already look and act like them!" He spat violently.

"Calm yourself, Srulko. There's no reason to be insulting. I'll do my best."

"You'll have to do better than your best! You promise me here, in the name of our departed Grandfather of blessed memory, that the Mandels will move in with us. You'll do it for the times I used to change your diapers; for the times I rocked you to sleep when you screamed like a spoiled little brat, which you were; for the . . ." Srulko might have continued were it not for Uncle Moritz's solemn promise to effect the desired change. He had learned long ago that it was well-nigh impossible to sway the old man from a given course.

The Mandels moved in with us. Srulko was contented. I was happy. Everyone was satisfied. Uncle Moritz had to make two pairs of brown, calf-leather boots for the Standartenführer. As it was, he gladly intervened in our behalf. He only regretted to have sacrificed the last of his stock of the finest calf-hide; he had intended to use it when a *real* emergency arose.

As time went on, we realized that Grandfather had made the right decision. The Mandels, Nora's Uncle Max and her cousin Hayim, were quiet but cordial people whom we grew to love as our very own. Grandfather was especially pleased because Max Mandel belonged to his Hasidic circle. They convened their study group frequently, and we often witnessed the heated scholarly sessions as the Hasidim argued the intricate points of the Law. At first I was startled that those bearded scholars seemed unconcerned, even oblivious, to the affairs about them. In time I grew to appreciate, even cherish, those sessions; the singsong dialogue and ancient wisdom.

They were simple, peace-loving men. In their unique thirst for learning, the Hasidim had tried to assert the claims of the heart as opposed to the dictates of the mind. They zealously pursued their struggle against excessive legalism and intellectualism. Theirs was a simple faith. It was to become a shield against the swastika. For the Hasid it was never sufficient to merely indulge in the interpretive commentary of the Mishnah or the Gemara; they took it upon themselves to reinterpret the famous passages, as only tsaddikim—the wisest of the wise—could afford to do. I learned and I remembered.

Several months had gone by. The Verpflegungskompanie, and with it Boost and our temporary "security," left the ancient castle. Before his departure, Boost gave me his home address. He made me promise to visit with him and his family at Eisenbahnstrasse 134 in Leipzig when the war ended. "Better days will come, my boy," he said as we embraced while the long column of Wehrmacht equipment stood ready to move out, "and when they do, Willi, we must resume on equal terms. Perhaps, my boy, it will be you who will have to come to my aid then, who knows."

"You must come back, Herr Unteroffizier. There are many things I have to tell you."

"Keep all those things in your heart, Willi." The merciless formation began to move. "Keep them there, and they will give you strength in the struggle ahead."

"I shall never forget you!"

"Remember!" Boost gently pushed me aside. He jumped onto the driver's seat of the covered wagon and disappeared around the corner of Zamkowa and past the ancient castle. Like all things in war, Boost's departure was abrupt. It was felt by all of us.

But we were in for a far greater shock when, early one morning in August, we found ourselves surrounded by a triple layer of barbed wire, guarded by the Lithuanian SS mercenaries. Until then, although living in the Jewish section of town, we could come and go within the allotted curfew hours. Now the sudden isolation of endless rolls of jagged wire.

An important announcement was proclaimed by the Gauleiter through his mouthpiece the Sturmbannführer, who became the new Commandant of the Jewish sector. He, in turn, spoke through the representative of the Judenrat, Mr. Warszawski. (The dignity and honor of an SS officer would suffer if he were to have contact with an inferior person, even if only through a spoken word.) Warszawski's announcement said, in effect, that only working parties would be allowed to leave the fenced-in section, and then only when accompanied by the Militia. There would be a more stringent curfew, seven o'clock to be exact, and anyone found on the street after that would be shot.

"This is an affront to human dignity!" Grandfather shouted to Uncle Moritz as he nervously paced up and down the room. For the first time in many months we began to feel hunger at home, particularly since I had lost the position with the Verpflegungskompanie. As the supplies dwindled, Mother was scarcely able to purchase what we needed for one day—not only because there was little money left, but also because black market prices were rising. Roman had occasionally been able to smuggle some food into the ghetto, as other "Aryan-looking" Jews had done. But when the wire fence was put up and sentries were posted around it, this became virtually impossible.

"The Sturmbannführer said to me, 'Moritz, you are a damned good Jew, fact is I often regret you weren't born an Aryan. I can confide in you, can't I? I will tell you now that we will have rigid controls over the ghetto from this day on. If we find any Jew outside the ghetto—and we can always tell a Jew by his Semitic features—he will be put to death. Death is the only penalty feared by men. No matter how miserable they are, they want to go on living.' "

"But Uncle Moritz, Roman looks like an Aryan and speaks like a Pole. How will they know that he is a Jew?"

"The Gestapo has its informers even among our own people, Wilek. It's brother against brother now."

"But what if one is not denounced by informers?" I insisted.

Uncle Moritz hesitated for a moment, and with sadness in his voice, he went on. "The Gestapo knows all about us there is to know. They will catch a suspect and they will apply the genital test. That will show them whether or not he is a Jew."

"What is the 'genital test'?"

"I hope you will never have to learn what it means, any of you."

Mother wept, Roman was defiant, and Grandfather kept pacing back and forth without solving anything.

A large crowd stood in front of the Judenrat building. Soldiers in black uniforms, the SS silver skull on their starched collars, surrounded the building, their guns ready. Several Gestapo officials holding a prisoner—allegedly a Jew apprehended outside the ghetto—were in Warszawski's office. There were rumors that an exemplary trial was to be conducted there, and the ghetto population was strongly "invited" to attend. Driven by curiosity, I became one of the spectators, pushed into the large reception room by the mass of people intent on witnessing the "trial." There, a slightly built man, rather insignificant and not at all heroic, kept on assuring his antagonists of his innocence.

"I am not a Jew! I am not a Jew!" he repeated endlessly. When his assertions did not effect a response, he resorted to stronger argumentation. "Why this is absurd, this accusation. And not only absurd and unfounded, but quite abusive. I, a Jew? Show me the face of the individual who sold you this preposterous lie!"

But all his exclamations and pleadings were of no avail. Once the Bureau decided to make an example of someone, guilty or innocent, there was no escape. Sturmbannführer Meier had no desire to relinquish what promised to become an unusually entertaining session at the "court," especially since he was to assume the function of judge and jury. Besides, he looked forward to a promotion he thought long overdue.

The spacious assembly hall of the Judenrat building held approximately one hundred and fifty people. Sturmbannführer Meier sat at a long table facing the crowd; at his right and left stood his underlings. Facing his judges, stood the prisoner; to his left was Warszawski, and beside him the official interpreter.

Sturmbannführer Meier was busy writing on a small pad. The prisoner trembled and pleaded his innocence. Meier scarcely noticed the frightened man. He was busy preparing his "case." When he finally finished, he turned to the audience and said, pointing at the prisoner:

"This Jew was apprehended today outside the ghetto limits, despite the strict order of the Judenrat that no Jew is to leave the ghetto without proper authorization. He did not wear the identification armband. He ran when challenged by one of my men to give himself up. Presently, he has the audacity to refuse the admission of his guilt."

The Sturmbannführer paused for a moment, only to continue in his forcefully dignified manner, reading from the notes he had jotted down moments ago. The few paragraphs Meier recited were written in the usual involved style employed by his people, and the interpreter was careful to wait for the participle or the infinitive terminating Meier's sentence before commencing to translate. His remarks ended with the customary summation:

"You are herewith charged with a fourfold crime: eins, leaving the ghetto premises without authorization; zwei, trying to conceal your identity by not wearing an armband; drei, refusing to respond to the challenge of the occupation forces; vier, knowingly jeopardizing the safety of your brethren."

The charges were read with the familiar tempo of goose-stepping boots. The Sturmbannführer's concern for the well-being of the ghetto inhabitants sounded almost genuine.

The prisoner stood silent. He realized that his fate was being sealed by this well-mannered Gestapo officer. He thought of ways to convince his judges of his innocence, but gradually understood that they were determined to use him as an example. The news of the trial and his subsequent punishment would serve as a useful deterrent for would-be escapees. He was startled by the stern voice of the Sturmbannführer:

"The prisoner will state his name!"

"My name is Franek Piecha."

"Where was the prisoner apprehended?" Meier's eyes pierced the frightened man.

"I was, I was . . ." It was a strain for the victim of twenty-four hours of ceaseless questioning to visualize the exact location and all the events leading up to his confinement and trial, but the scene came gradually to his mind.—He got off the train from Lodz, cheerfully anticipating his visit with his aunt, Mrs. Bosiacki. The traveling bag weighed his right arm slightly downward, as he directed himself toward the droshke stand. He thought with delight how he would refresh with a cool shower and a change of clothing. It was then that he heard a voice shouting "Jude! Jude! Jude!" The voice came closer, and he suddenly realized that he was being pursued, and moments later he found himself in the midst of a jeering mob. A formidable kick to his left thigh caused him to stumble forward. His bag fell from his hand and he ran frightened. Within moments, he was in the strong grip of a native policeman. There were questions and more questions, apparently inadequately answered, because he was taken to Gestapo headquarters.

It was a dreadful night Franek spent in the basement cell of the Seventh Bureau jail. He could not understand why he was there after having explained his identity, substantiated by the bonafide Polizeiausweis and Reisegenehmigung. Everyone had to take out a police certificate of identification those days. And one had to apply for a traveling permit to go anywhere within a five kilometer radius of one's home. Franek was a God-fearing Christian from a good family. His father, Dr. Olek Piecha, was formerly Professor at the University of Lodz. He was afraid his interrogators would know that his father had gone to Russia and from there to England, to join the Polish Armed Forces in exile. He was frightened by the many eyes penetrating him. The spotless Gestapo uniforms and their shiny boots unnerved him. But above all he was tired and annoyed. He was aware that he looked like a Semite! But he was no Jew! Was he to tell them the names of his aunt, of his friends, perhaps? They would surely identify

47

him! But Franek was afraid. "Merciful Virgin Mary," he thought to himself, "what if I might implicate my friends also?" Franek kept his silence.

"Come now, answer the question!" The sound of Meier's voice returned him to reality. "Tell the assembled where you were at the time of your apprehension!" Meier addressed him directly.

"I was near the railroad station."

"And what were you doing near the station?" Meier continued relentlessly.

"I was walking toward the droshke stand."

"Now then, were you aware that you were not permitted to go outside the ghetto limits without special authorization?" Meier was quite pleased with the last statement, that of "authority," and he repeated the latter part of the sentence before the prisoner could reply. "Did you have an official permit from the authorities?"

"No, of course not," said Franek, with a disconcerting lack of equivocation, "I did not realize that I needed one."

"And you did not think that you might be apprehended and brought to justice?"

"No," replied Franek sincerely, "I had no reason to fear apprehension. I am not a Jew!" He mustered all his strength and courage for the last statement.

"Did you not run when accused of being a Jew?"

"Maybe I did, maybe I didn't. I can't remember exactly." Franek was at his wit's end and Meier was sufficiently a judge of men to sense it. His instinct told him that the victim was at the breaking point.

"If you are innocent of the charges brought against you, if you are not a Jew, will you let the court examine you in accordance with the law. You must submit to the genital test." Meier's conciliatory statement sounded as though he were also fed up with the proceedings and he wished to end them. In all sincerity, the prisoner replied affirmatively:

"Yes, of course." And as he uttered the three fatal words, it came to him, with the suddenness of death, that he had been circumcised in his infancy—"for sanitary reasons," they had said.

Franek Piecha was hanged in the middle of the market square, in front of the ancient synagogue, and his limp body was displayed for a total of forty-eight hours—for all to see, for all to remember.

The Jews considered Franek's death an oddity, a kind of "poetic justice." Humorous anecdotes circulated among them as a result of the trial. People chuckled as they whispered to one another, "Franek gave his life for our cause, and he wasn't even a Piotrkover. He was the first goy to give his life in the ghetto al kiddush hashem, for our faith, without being entitled to a proper burial and a kaddish." I wondered whether his shadow would be allowed to return and mingle with the shadows of our departed. After all, one shadow more or less made little difference to us, but to him it might have meant a great deal.

The night following the Piecha trial the ghetto experienced still another of the many ingenious methods devised to speed up the resettlement of the inferior races, the Judenreinigung. The method was introduced under the strange-sounding name, the Rollkommando.

A few trucks, loaded with Lithuanian SS troops, drove through the ghetto streets in the late hours of the night. Unexpectedly, the trucks came to a halt on Silna Street and the eager mercenaries piled out rapidly onto the street. Disciplined efficiency was the essence of the operation. As they started toward the various homes, their assignment became obvious. From behind the safety of window shutters, we watched and listened. Neighbors were quickly rounded up and herded into the courtyard of the old synagogue. Most of them were half-naked and not altogether awake. On occasion, the hunters stopped long enough to molest the more attractive women and young girls. Those who resisted were quieted with the butt of a rifle. The hunt went on for several hours. Women were violated and homes were looted. It was not beneath the station of the invader to yield to his natural impulses so long as he knew that his victim would not live long enough to relate her experience.

During the latter part of the raid our family, along with many others, huddled quietly in the basement of Grandfather's house. On Silna Street, only one block away, our friends and acquaintances were being driven from their possessions, but we remained passive, terrorized by the mere thought that the affair might not end on Silna Street. We prayed to our merciful God, blessed be He, that the invaders be satisfied with their booty and leave us in peace.

"Whatever happens," Mr. Mandel whispered to Nora, "we must not do anything to antagonize the Germans. They leave us alone and we leave them alone," he rationalized.

"Remember, our sages bid us to live, as they proclaim:

"I call heaven and earth
to witness against you this day,
that I have set before thee
life and death, the blessing
and the curse; therefore
choose life, that thou mayest
live, thou and thy seed . . ."

"Jude verrecke!" ("Jew drop dead!") the SS shouts were heard even to the very corners of our hideout. Worse than the sound of the swastika pledge was the guilt we were to carry as a helpless people. After the first Rollkommando had ended, a queer silence on the ghetto streets; a silence louder than the shouts of pain on the previous night.

But the invaders came a step closer to their final goal; Piotrkow was well on its way to becoming Judenfrei (free of Jews).

There were rumors. There was fear. Above all, there was congestion and the constant anxiety of the ghetto mind. All four together had the aspect of a *Ghetto Apocalypse*. With the over-all conditions becoming worse, happy songs were rarely heard. That was a bad sign, because the Jewish people were a musical people. But the Hasid still sang his praises of God, the Kiddush, on Sabbath eve. Not even the constant rattle of the SS rifles was able to disrupt the majesty of the Jew's prayer.

Soon a new song was born in the ghetto. It was hummed by every person able to carry a tune. Like all things in war, it came suddenly, as if carried by the shadows.

WHITHER SHALL I GO . . . ? *
 Whither shall I go . . . ?
 When every exit is shut.
 Whither shall I go . . . ?
 When everywhere stands a guard.
 Whither shall I go . . . ?
 I am told to stay put.
 Wherever I might turn,
 They tell me "Jew remain."
 And return to your lot.

It was an old question. There were ghettos in the past, there were Hamans, and there was suffering. But it was much simpler to tell a story of suffering than to experience it. The stories were old, but the reality was imminent. And there was no Moses in view to utter the famous words: "Let my people go!"

The people needed a miracle. And while they waited and prayed, there was more fear, there was more congestion, and there were rumors. And in all the fear and congestion, amid the rumors of imminent doom, there resounded the doleful melody, reverberating from every spiral of the barbed wire fence: WHITHER SHALL I GO . . . ?

* See Appendix.

*Much have they afflicted me from
    my youth up,
Let Israel now say;
Much have they afflicted me from
    my youth up;
But they have not prevailed against
    me.*

PSALMS 129:1–2

It did not come as a surprise. Our money was finally and
irrevocably gone. Mother attempted to find buyers for her
linen or the fine feather bedding, which we would scarcely
miss, but such articles were available in great abundance.
There was still demand for silver, but Mother kept hers religiously hidden from view. It had been a wedding present
from Father. She would not sell it; not so soon at least.

"Can you imagine? What do they take me for? Ten
zlotys they offered me for three sets of linen!"

"Calm yourself child," Grandmother tried to keep her
composure, "you mustn't worry so much. We'll get by somehow."

"Ten zlotys! We could get two pounds of potatoes for
that amount of money. And that's one meal. One meal for
three sets of linen."

"Shah . . . the children."

"The money is gone. We have to do something."

"Let's take out the silver," Grandmother suggested.

52

"That won't be necessary." Grandfather stepped out of the bedroom, carrying a small, blue-white metal box, the familiar box with the map of Israel and the inscription "make the wilderness bloom." Every Jewish home had such a box. Jewish children and adults alike collected their tzeddakah, so that some day the Jews could redeem and reclaim Israel; that was the spirit of Keren Kayemet L'Israel.

"No! You mustn't, Srulko!" Grandmother exclaimed.

"Israel can wait, we can't. If we starve we wouldn't be good to anyone. This, I feel, Israel would not want to happen. It is our holy duty to survive, if possible. And if the meager saving which we have here can help us in this task, I feel that we are obliged to take it. Israel will understand, and the Almighty, blessed be His Name, will forgive us."

"But Srulko, this is sacred money!"

"Give me the key, Sarah." Grandfather called her by her given name only during the rare moments of crisis. "Give me the key, I say, we will replenish all we took if we live, and if we don't survive, I shall answer for it when I am called before our Maker."

Reluctantly, Grandmother handed the small key to her husband. She looked away when he turned it, emptying the box onto the tablecloth. He counted the small coins.

"Nine zlotys and thirty-five groszy," he said sadly. "It wouldn't have purchased much land in Israel anyhow."

Grandmother ignored her husband for one whole week after his sinful deed. The money provided one inadequate meal for all of us, and the silver had to be sold soon thereafter.

"What will happen after this is gone?" Mother really did not expect anyone to answer.

"I have an idea!" Grandfather exclaimed. "It's high time I pay another visit to our cousin the shoemaker!"

It was then that Uncle Moritz became a frequent visitor on Zamkowa 20. He had a wife and two children at home, but he spent most of his evenings with us. And each time he came, he brought with him some food for our families. Also, he always remembered to bring a little something for Nora. In fact, it was evident that Nora was the primary cause of his frequent visits.

In spite of the many hardships, Nora grew more beautiful each day. She was kept at home most of the time for fear that she would fall victim of the plundering Militia. Many an innocent Jewess was dishonored and discreetly disposed of by the mercenaries.

Whenever Mandel admonished her for staying out longer than necessary, Nora promptly replied, "I can take care of myself, Uncle Max."

But Max Mandel knew that it was easier said than done. Force was used in the name of "law." No one dared to question the "law." The mercenaries plundered Jewish homes. They shot Jews dead in the street from the guard towers which had been erected by Jewish labor. Men, women, and children were tortured and insulted. Literally hundreds of Jews disappeared in the name of the "law."

One evening, all the adults had gone to the Judenrat assembly. Roman went with Mother, for they were to discuss some new labor laws concerning all able-bodied Jews in the ghetto. Felusia was asleep; Hayim and I were busy preparing our Humash portion for the heder. Uncle Moritz came as usual. We appreciated his visits those days, because he seldom came empty-handed.

"Shouldn't you boys be in bed now?"

"After our homework is done, Uncle Moritz."

He sat down close to Nora. They talked about irrelevant things. Hayim left the living room to seek quiet and concentration, and I followed.

Uncle Moritz had had a successful week. He made three pairs of boots; two for the Brigadeführer and one for the officer's wife. For his accomplishments, he was treated to a few glasses of good German Schnapps in the SS headquarters. He was in happy spirits.

"Nora, you're a beautiful woman." He moved closer to her and placed his arm around her waist.

"You mustn't, please." She tried to disengage herself from his firm hold.

"Please, just a little bit," he whispered. His voice had an unpleasant, hissing sound, and his hand reached for her breast.

Nora had tolerated the situation thus far, because it was inconceivable that Uncle Moritz would dare to make amorous advances. Still, out of fear and pity, she hesitated.

"I've waited for this moment with all the passion and longing, my little dove," he pressed her tightly to himself, kissed her mouth, and let his left hand wander to the warmth of her thighs.

"Please, Uncle Moritz, please go home before you do something regrettable."

Moritz rushed toward her, suddenly resolved that no loss would be greater. He tore the garments from her trembling body and Nora screamed. I ran into the living room and I saw Uncle Moritz holding Nora firmly around her waist. She was bending backward as far as she was able. He aimed at pressing his hungry lips to her breasts, but could not quite make it in the scuffle.

"Do something, Wilek! Call someone! Help me!"

Moritz saw me standing in the doorway. He released his hold and, with a resounding slap, shouted, "You little bitch! Wait till *they* take you! You'll be sorry for what you did!"

He rushed from the living room and I could hear his hurried steps as he ran down the wooden stairs.

Exhausted from the encounter, Nora sat sobbing on the floor. Mechanically, I picked up her garments which were scattered about the room and helped her put them on. She was momentarily in a daze, but quickly regained her composure.

"We mustn't tell about this," she pleaded, "no one must know what happened."

"I promise, I swear I won't tell!" I assured her, kissing

the tears from her cheeks. "Hayim is already asleep, so no one will know."

"Now I've made Uncle Moritz angry and he won't come and bring us food any longer," Nora said wearily.

"Let's wait and see what was decided at the meeting of the Judenrat tonight, Nora. We have done without him before, and we can do it again." Things would be different from then on; both Nora and I had realized that much.

When morning came we had learned that the situation had worsened. All able-bodied men of the ghetto were to begin forced labor immediately. The two glass factories, Kara and Hortensia, were short of men to produce bottles for drugs and beverages. The peacetime output of the two factories was impressive, but they said it had doubled when the enemy took over.

Very early in the Nazi occupation the Poles who worked in industry had received preferential treatment. However, as soon as occupation was secure, the Gauleiter's patriotic thriftiness imposed annoying restrictions on Polish labor. "More work and less pay" was the Gauleiter's principal innovation. Things went well for a while, but soon the workers began to leave their jobs. No one knew where they went, but there were persistent rumors about the newly formed Polish resistance. For every man gone from his job, one Nazi war function remained unfulfilled and their war effort suffered. By the very fact that he would abandon his post at the factory, the young worker declared his fight against the invader.

But the enemy was swift to strike back. If a man were to leave his job, his mother or his father, his wife—in the event he was married—or his children would suffer torment and, ultimately, death. Any man who dared desert his "duty" marked his loved ones for reprisal.

Yet the Gauleiter had not been swift enough. Although the prospect of reprisals discouraged many an aspiring partisan, sufficient harm had already been done; numerous machines stood idle at the two glass factories, waiting for someone, skilled or unskilled, to put them to work for the great cause, the Third Reich.

It was in utter desperation that the Gauleiter conceived the idea of a "working Jew." Everyone knew that no Jew was capable of work, everyone from the Führer in *Mein Kampf* down to the chauffeur in the Sturmbannführer's household. But this was an emergency, and theories are often forgotten, if not refuted, during national crises. Only the old and the very young were left at home to wonder eternally about their fate.

Herr Seemann and Herr Forster were the two civilian administrators of the factory. No one knew where they came from, nor did we know what their connections were with the Seventh Bureau. The day we were formally informed of our new status, "working Jew," we stood at attention, carefully measuring these new adversaries.

Herr Forster stepped forward and shouted an order, thereby establishing his superiority as the work camp's Deputy Commandant. All was silent. He ascended the makeshift rostrum. Attention centered on his massive structure, his curly blond hair, and his cloud-gray eyes. When he made his only attempt at being comical, the audience somehow did not share his sense of humor. This increased his awkwardness and he earned the nickname Golem, the idiot.

"Juden," Forster exclaimed, "you will work now for the Third Reich. We expect you to work well, and you will be treated likewise. Work will commence in three shifts, each eight hours long. You will rest half an hour during your shift. In payment for your work the Judenrat will receive provisions for the ghetto. Anyone who will do outstanding work will receive special rewards. We are generous with the industrious and the faithful."

"He is generous, did you hear that?" I whispered to Roman. "It's not so bad after all."

"Quiet there!" Herr Seemann shouted into the crowd. "This is another thing you have to learn, verfluchtes Gesindel," (he addressed us less kindly using the language of Nazi Kultur) "you have to learn to be silent when you are spoken to by your superiors! You will keep your mouths shut whenever you are spoken to, or else."

It was Seemann who attracted our attention initially. His small eyes measured our ranks constantly, as though searching for something, and the ugly scar on his right cheek made him repulsive and frightening at the same time. Knowing the Commandant to be a buffoon, his second-in-command earned our respect as the man to watch and avoid. He was christened respectfully Mamzehr, the bastard.

Neither Golem nor Mamzehr had ever before been trusted with such absolute responsibility. Their newly acquired awareness of being masters over the lives of inferior beings overwhelmed them. This was their first opportunity to realize their full potential, to truly devote themselves to the fascinating game of playing tyrants.

That night Grandfather and I discussed the new circumstances. We took stock of the eventful past and had no illusions about the future. First there had been the identifying armband with the star of David; but even then many were able to continue passing as gentiles. Next, the penalty of death for removing the armband; but many defied this for a moment of borrowed freedom and dignity. Then, the truckloads of barbed wire wound around the Judenstadt. The Lithuanian sentries. Towers, and one large gate on Zielna Street marking the central point of the ghetto. Tomorrow a new phase, forced labor.

"Take things as they come, my boy," he tried to reassure me. "Life's burdens never lighten, we simply learn to live with them as time moves on."

I understood what he was saying but was deep in my secret worry. During the time I had worked for the Supply Company, I had met some gentile boys my own age from far off neighborhoods who gathered at the fence to beg scraps. I always managed to save something for them, and eventually we became friends. Passing as a shaygetz, a ruffian, I had enjoyed safety in their company. I walked proudly on the sidewalk without ducking blows, without eluding stones, and without having to run at the sound of "brudny żydzie!"—in the language of our hostile countrymen, "dirty Jew!"

Tomorrow was the test. We would be marched through the gates into the forbidden section of town accompanied by a few well armed guards. I knew my friends would not miss the opportunity to line the streets the first day the Jews were being led to work.

Grandfather prayed half the night and Mother and Nora wept as Roman and I were herded into formation. I marched deep in the middle of the ranks, hoping the remarks of my former companions would not reach me or that they might fail to see me altogether. But there was no escape. As we marched the whispers grew into shouts.

"Juden! Juden! The Jews are coming! Now you carry the cross for a while!"

There were some who stood by silently, and we thanked them in silence.

The column reached the familiar section of town. From a distance I saw them all. My heartbeat quickened, and like an animal sensing danger I knew that things were to happen on this day that had never happened before. I wished that it were all over for me rapidly, with as little pain as possible. But as in most nightmares, time passed slowly. One . . . two . . . three . . . four . . . one . . . two . . . three . . . four . . . At last, we marched past the "reviewing" stand.

All of them were there. There was Tadzik, Yanek, Zbyszek, Mietek, and all the others. Some held whips fashioned from branches of trees. They did not see me at once. "Jude! Jude!" They used their twigs on our rank and no one stopped them.

Eventually I was noticed.

"See the filthy Jew," Mietek shouted, "what did I say? Now it's all out in the open! He lied! He made fools of us!"

There were those who looked at me in disbelief.

"Is it true, Wilek, are you a Jew? What are you doing there wearing an armband? Take that armband off. Come out here! You belong with us!"

For this moment alone I wished that I were not a Jew. But I was as much Jew as they were gentile. I wanted to explain, to tell them that my people were the people of Shem, and their people were the people of Japheth. Shem and Japheth were brothers. But there was no time.

Suddenly it was too much. I screamed and pushed my way out of the formation and through my tormentors. Then I ran. I tore my armband from my sleeve and ran.

There were shouts of "Halt!" and the sound of pursuing boots. I could only think, I must get away. I must get away. Out of breath, I redoubled my efforts but they caught me easily. Blow upon blow landed with uncanny accuracy. I was picked up and tossed on the pavement, but each time the pain was less and the whole world seemed to reverberate with the sound "Jude! Jude! Jude!"

There was darkness and light and the most fantastic colors. I fell and the pain disappeared.

During this semiconscious state, I heard a rare sound. "He is still our guy, he will always remain one of us." I did not recognize the voice, but the sweet sounds were enough.

Later, at home, I kept repeating to myself, "It isn't as though you have been smashed to bits, you know. There is only a bruise or two here and there and a sting of pain."

"Time is the best healer, my son," Mother murmured,

patting my head, "before you get to be twenty-one, the hurt will be long gone and forgotten."

Indeed, time and hard work did exercise their balsamic effect on our bruises, although pain remained deep in the soul. Days grew inscrutably long and increasingly wearisome. Gradually, we learned to accept.

Among themselves, in subdued voices, the Jews attempted to lighten their burden by ridiculing the enemy. Innumerable jokes were circulated in the ghetto. And although the macabre humor did not impede the success of the enemy, it was a moral victory for the defeated.

Late in 1941 Nora came down with a fever. Mother would not send for a doctor for fear we would be quarantined. It was typhus. On the fifth day a dark red rash of elevated spots appeared. The temperature subsided considerably during the second week; however, on the fifteenth day Nora became delirious again. Mother applied a cold towel as the sole medication. The men prayed.

"He is after me . . . keep him from me . . . don't let him get me! Don't let him get me!"

"No one will harm you, little one. No one will harm you," Mother repeated mechanically.

"I don't want to go, I don't want to go," Nora pleaded in the monotonous wail of the sick.

"You're staying right here, my baby, and we are not going to leave you." She placed another compress on Nora's forehead. Eventually, Nora slept.

"There is nothing we can do but wait and hope for the best. The fever must break soon," Grandmother spoke from experience.

We stayed up all night with the delirious girl. When morning came we were greeted by a faint, but determined demand: "I am hungry. I would like to eat." Grandmother had been right. The last bit of fever had wrestled the sickness from Nora's body.

We thanked the Almighty for His boundless mercies. "Blessed be He." There would be no quarantine, no unpleasant encounters with the Department of Health. We were prepared for Nora's demand. Special foodstuffs were kept on hand for her convalescence.

Soon, the flower was in bloom again, more beautiful and incalculably stronger for having experienced partial death. The Hasidim rejoiced and sang praises to the One and Only.

But strange are the ways of the Almighty, blessed be He. As we rejoiced at the newly given life, Father's friend arrived in the ghetto from the east. He brought us news—part of Father's diary. That very evening, as we were all gathered in the living room, Mother read, word for word, stopping only until her eyes cleared and her voice stopped trembling.

෴

And it came to pass . . .

The sages lament, when the
Gods struggled, men suffered
Excruciating pain and boundless woe.
And sorrow begot sorrow . . .

And it came to pass . . .

Dark shadows fell upon the
Sun, and it was dark, and
Mankind fell into severest cold, and
Pain was rampant, and giants fell . . .

And it came to pass . . .

62

The Æsir burst with the
Thunder of the battling gods,
While mortals froze astonished,
And the sages wept . . .

The godly man is perished out of the
*   earth,*
And the upright among men is no more;
They all lie in wait for blood;
They hunt every man his brother
*   with a net.*

MICAH 7:2

My dearly beloved,

If we should fail to meet again, perhaps by chance someone may bring you this sign of life from me. You shall know
that during the most trying hours I was with you, thinking of
the happy moments and anticipating the time of our reunion.
I want you to know that in the despair of separation I would
have gladly given up my life but for the thoughts of you. The
will to live was stronger than resignation. Although everything seemingly important had been taken from me, I thank
God for the many happy memories He left me, for they were
a blessing indeed in times of hardship.

You may already know that my entire division was imprisoned by the Soviets as soon as we crossed their border.
They imprisoned us, after having offered asylum. I can see it
clearly now—it is all a master plan for the future conquest of
Poland. Such are the fortunes of war: intrigue, conspiracy,
and unfulfilled promises.

During the past few months I have searched my youth as

far back as my memory could take me. I recall things I never thought important. I remember a Latin phrase the teacher made us memorize, for which we ardently despised him. In my sleep, I can hear the words distinctly: *mortui cura et dolore carent*, "the dead are free from anxiety and pain." Time and again I hear the same theme. The Romans were wise to have put it so plainly and beautifully. As things grew worse, I envied our departed ancestors. The effects of ill fortune are overpowering. I chuckle to myself now, as I realize how soon I was ready to succumb; but I learned to accept my lot and I adjusted. I want you to know that I hold no ill will toward Uncle Markus, from America, and I do not want you to blame him or Aunt Haya for our misfortune. Each man acts according to the dictates of his own conscience, and I am convinced that Uncle Markus tried his best—may God be merciful to him if he did not. Most of all, I must tell you that our family is in no way unique. I have met many whose plans of emigrating were shattered by the Blitzkrieg.

After the Germans invaded the Soviet Union last June, we were transported in cattle wagons to the north. We arrived in a Siberian labor camp on the eve of my thirty-third birthday. My thoughts were with you. Meanwhile, the train rolled slowly onto a siding with a deliberate squeak of its brakes, which came to a loud crescendo only to die out suddenly as bumper collided with bumper and we came to a final stop. The sudden noise startled me out of my reverie. We tried to see outside through the narrow cracks in the wagon wall, but all we were able to perceive was a barbed-wire fence, ominously pointed with ugly thorns.

At the time of our arrival in camp everyone's nerves were pitched to the utmost. Our stomachs had shrunk, and we were so on edge that the slightest provocation could have caused a riot. We found it difficult to show good manners at a time like this. It was dark inside the wagon, with only narrow streaks of light filtering through the worn walls.

"Take your damned foot off my face!" someone exclaimed.

There was a commotion. A cloud of dust mingled with the sun rays.

"Sorry, friend."

"Just watch your step!" was the brief retort, and then things were quiet again.

They were rugged and mean individuals, these men who had traveled for over three weeks in worse conditions than cattle have.

I was never one to associate with crowds. But, ironic as it may seem, our close quarters possessed the unique virtue of keeping us warm. I guess even this was one of the paradoxes of life: although every man was concerned only about himself, the subzero temperature compelled one to care for the other.

Each man in his own simple way, asked himself: "Can this be the end?" Some felt regret, some relief, others experienced fear—common thoughts when things seem to be approaching an end. But almost every man expected to go on living.

If it were not for the leather jacket you managed to hand me on the day of my departure, my ribs would have been fractured from the many blows I received. As it was, the heavily padded leather softened them to some degree. The jacket had only one major drawback: its warmth attracted lice. I felt them crawling all over me and I was unable to scratch. They invaded my clothing overnight and fed on the precious blood still left in me. I was thankful for the warmth the jacket provided despite the handicap. And after a while I grew accustomed to my comrades' brutality, as well as to the persistency of the gnawing parasites.

I guess everyone wondered what the camp would be like; the food and the work. Would we sleep on a half-way decent straw-sack again? Would our keepers feed us some warm soup? I could feel it slide into my shrunken, freezing stomach! What ecstasy!

Someone lighted a match. Its flicker seemed to bring heat to the most distant corners of the wagon. A solemn, thin face looked haggard and mysterious from behind the glowing cigarette butt. Shadows of faces nearby expressed their greed silently as his moistened fingers held onto the slowly dying match. The hand trembled as the flame died gradually. I was thankful for not having acquired the habit. Men are slaves of many vices.

I might have appreciated the lighted match. The tips of my fingers were almost numb. There was little breath left to warm the cupped palms of my shivering hands. Nor could I put them in the pockets of my jacket, which were full of odds and ends for personal use. I guarded these with my life. The only luggage I possessed was there. Nothing else was left me, except feelings and memories, and I dreaded the day when even that might be taken from me.

"Get out, you filthy pack!"

The abrupt command was shouted by a stocky, well-fed, red-nosed Soviet corporal as he slid open the doors of our wagon with much noise and little ceremony. He seemed to be in charge. His underlings stood a short distance away. Daylight penetrated the wagon with a blinding suddenness. As we grew accustomed to it, we perceived the guards standing by with bayonets fixed onto their antiquated rifles. We hesitated.

"You Polish swine, get down here or I'll whip the skin off your filthy carcasses!"

He swung the whip with a loud crack. In the resulting commotion I lost my balance and fell. I raised my arms upward, desperately trying to hold on to something, when the jacket slid off and disappeared in the mass of rushing men. When I finally got up, the jacket was gone. I collected a few lost articles from the wagon floor which must have fallen out of the pockets. Hastily, I hid them in the folds of my shirt. The corporal's whip found a mark.

As I joined my comrades in formation, I noticed one of them wearing the jacket—my leather jacket. I wanted to shout, to accuse, to beg. But the bayonets looked too dangerous for complaints. I thought of the objects tucked away safely under my shirt. In them I found peace and consolation; after all, the lice went with the jacket.

I had never imagined that so much evil existed in this God's universe. We stood in formation and the corporal reviewed the wretched file. Meanwhile some of the guards climbed onto the wagons to make the customary search. They reported three dead and one barely alive. All four bodies were thrown from the wagon, where they lay motionless on the cold ground. The soldiers laughed.

"You there!"

The voice was directed toward our ranks. Instinctively I pulled my head down between my shoulders and pretended not to hear.

"You there, you with the fancy jacket," the voice persisted, "step out here!"

Mechanically, I started to move toward the voice, mentally still in possession of the jacket. When I looked up, I saw its new owner step out of the ranks. Timidly, he stopped a few paces from the guard.

"Closer, come closer, you dog!" the little corporal shouted. "Turn around!" He pulled off his warm woolen gloves and caressed the soft hide with expert fingers. I had a premonition that no good was to come of all this.

"What's your name?" the corporal bellowed at the trembling man.

"Sergeant Kazimir Bieda, Third Cavalry Regiment!" The sergeant might have clicked his heels together, were it not for the fact that his feet were bare.

"Get back in line!" The man obeyed. His puzzled face

showed that he expected more to come, and we were all certain the little corporal was not one to disappoint him.

On our way towards the main camp we saw signs printed on buildings in large letters: RECEPTION CENTER—DISINFECTION—SUPPLIES. We went through a process known as "being received," after which we were divided into even groups and led to the barracks. Soon our overseers left. "You may as well make yourselves comfortable," the guard chuckled, "you're in for a long stay."

"I tell you men this is a decent work camp," a tall, bearded man remarked. He was a bricklayer from the Ukraine, an avowed foe of communism, and his name was Misha Grozny. He was among the Ukrainian volunteers who had joined the invading Germans in the hope of establishing an independent Republic of the Ukraine. But he soon learned that he would much rather suffer the consequences of betrayal than the arrogance of his alleged liberators. "Take a look at the stove, the fresh straw-sacks, and the decent furniture." There was also a table and two long benches. He placed his fingers to his lips, "This is better than many I have seen so far."

"We might have to pay dearly for this comfort," someone interjected cautiously.

"Take a look about a mile away from the camp," someone said. "There's a lot of forest."

Lumber camps were no novelty. We had heard of them. The quota of lumber expected daily of each worker made the camp more lethal than a hungry Siberian wolf.

"You worry too much; all you do is worry," interrupted an elderly man of rather dignified appearance; a stately gray beard covered the better half of his chest. "It isn't enough for you to worry yourselves; you frighten others with your silly talk. There is nothing to gain by your theorizing. Be smart, let time take its course."

"Listen to the prophet. All we need, under the circumstances, is a prophet who would remind us of the great truth and teach us right from wrong," someone remarked jokingly.

But the bearded old man became *our* "prophet," though no one took him seriously. The Prophet made sense. He was the only civilian prisoner in our group. Prior to the outbreak of the war he had been a teacher of a village high school along the Polish border. He told us the name of his village once, but I cannot recall whether it was Tcherny or Terna. Anyway, the name of a small town does not really matter. What matters is the reason for which the Prophet was sentenced to five years of hard labor before a People's Tribunal. He had committed a crime; upon having returned from America, where he had visited his brother, he expressed his admiration for that country publicly. He admired the people and their achievements. Impressed by the innumerable places of worship, he extolled the American youth for its active participation in religious services. He spoke often and freely. One day he was summoned to appear before the People's Tribunal to answer to the charge of treason. He was tried as a yevrey, a Jew, although he vainly attempted to defend his rights as a native son of this land. Only the martyred victims of the enemy earn the right to be called Russians, though they may forfeit their lives as Jews.

The Prophet seldom indulged in idle conversation and never complained. At times, when the men threatened to become restless, he interfered for the sake of harmony. I wanted to be close to this man so I could consult with him in case of need. I had to talk to someone. Perhaps I could even learn to trust him. It is important in this place of confinement to have an occasional exchange of thoughts or one could go mad. There is nothing else left us that gives a semblance of civilized society. I complained to the Prophet about my recent loss.

"Forget it. Put it out of your mind. Pretend you never had a jacket," he advised.

70

"I can't give up what's mine," I pleaded with the old man, trying to gain his approval for whatever was to come. He looked at me for a moment impassively, shrugged his shoulders, and turned away. The matter was closed for him.

I made an honest effort to heed the Prophet's counsel. I even silently learned to suffer the severe weather. The thief continued in possession of my jacket. I could not bear to see him enjoy the comfort which was rightfully mine. My wrath grew, may God forgive me. Even during the evenings of Bible readings, conducted by the Prophet, I could not help myself.

The Prophet read from Leviticus: "Thou shalt not hate thy brother in thy heart. Thou shalt not take vengeance, nor bear any grudge against the children of thy people, but thou shalt love thy neighbor as thyself: I am the Lord."

Even then, I countered with another passage: "Ye shall not steal, neither shall ye deal falsely, nor lie one to another. And ye shall not swear by my name falsely, so that thou profane the name of thy God: I am the Lord."

Although he did not tell me so directly, I sensed that the Prophet understood and sympathized with my feelings. He made no attempt to sway me from my course of action as I plotted the repossession of my property.

On the day after the Bible reading I did everything to attract the corporal's attention. I had resolved to make a deal with him. My opportunity presented itself late that afternoon when the corporal made his customary rounds to inspect the results of the day's work.

Hiding behind the stack of wood which represented my daily quota, I observed the little corporal as he slowly approached. The customary punishment for addressing a guard was a good lashing, but I decided to pursue my plan in the hope that the corporal's greed was greater than his fear of rules.

The little corporal choked with indecision when I addressed him. He was as frightened to make the contact as I was. I spoke quickly, with urgency in my voice:

"Corporal . . . the leather jacket . . . the one you liked, remember, on the day of our arrival . . . it's mine . . . really mine . . ."

"So?" He looked at me with the inherent distrust of a Kulak. He looked around cautiously. "So what?"

"I want it returned to me . . . it's mine and I want it back." My time was running short. I saw a second guard approaching.

"What do I care about your jacket and how do I know it's really yours," he snapped and turned to go.

"Wait, don't go yet," I caught him by the sleeve. "I can prove it to you . . . there is money hidden in it," I was telling the truth and he could sense it.

"Money? What money?" he attempted to sound indifferent. I looked him squarely in the eyes and sensed his shrewdness. "Where is the money?" he managed to snap at me while walking away.

"Get it back for me . . . get my jacket back and the money is yours!" I whispered, hoping that the approaching guard did not hear.

I knew not to divulge more. I remembered the Prophet's warning; the guards were unpredictable. I kept a bargaining position for as long as the corporal was curious and greedy.

The approaching guard was within hearing distance. Without a word, or the slightest indication of his intentions, the stocky little corporal walked briskly away. There was once again silence. There was bitter cold, as another Siberian night had come. I cried unto God for justice; "If thou at all take thy neighbor's garment to pledge, thou shalt restore it unto him by the time the sun goeth down; for that is his only covering, it is his garment for his skin; wherein shall he sleep, and it shall come to pass, when he crieth unto Me, that I will hear; for I am gracious."

I cried unto Him. But the cold wintry night came and I was left without my garment. And I fell into a restless sleep.

"Get up, you miserable pack!" The shouting of the guards put an end to one nightmare and started another.

"All right! Everybody out into the yard!" With the sound of the corporal's unpleasant voice, my thoughts returned once more to the jacket. We fell into groups of ten. The Prophet, the jacket thief Kazimir Bieda, myself, and seven other men comprised our work group. The little corporal came toward us.

"You're the foreman of this group from now." He pointed at me with a sly smile. It was a position which I did not covet. The corporal considered it a favor, and favors had to be paid for. There was also the grave responsibility of fulfilling the quota.

The work groups marched off to their assigned sectors. Our detachment followed the little corporal into the forest, a limitless, never-ending sea of pine. There were pines in all directions, covered with snow. Under different circumstances this might have been considered a beautiful sight. But frostbitten as we were, we were unable to admire the majestic beauty. All I could think of was how fortunate the man was who wore my leather jacket. His movements were not hindered by the rag wrappings the rest of us had used in order to keep out the wind.

Before the beginning of each working day we were to stand at attention while the corporal addressed us. It was wellnigh impossible to stand still with the temperature down at thirty degrees below zero. The men kept trotting in place.

Often I caught myself questioning the purpose of my fate. "How have I transgressed to invoke such punishment?" I thought, unable to understand. And the little corporal was also angry. He was a different kind of god. The camp had many gods. The upper echelons remained anonymous, but this only made the lesser gods, like our little corporal, all the more powerful, because their blows were imminent and their thundering voices were often heard.

"Swing your axes and get the saws going! You have a quota to fill! No quota, no food! No food and you're dead!" He stopped to read the impression made by his announcement. Then, as if moved by a sudden inspiration, he added, "and the world will be better off without the lot of you!" We worked while the guards sipped vodka abundantly. They amused themselves by observing how awkwardly we handled our work implements. They were Kulaks and they carried a strong dislike for city dwellers.

We were told that there would be special benefits for any group that produced above its quota. Ironically, we had not heard of anyone fulfilling the quota, much less surpassing it. No doubt our lesser gods expected personal rewards as well as praise from the higher deities for our efforts.

As the day progressed the little corporal became bolder in his inebriation. Each swallow of vodka added to his joviality and the bottle seemed bottomless. Toward the day's end our little god was totally drunk. Yet in this semiconscious state he was able to remember our bargain. He acted upon it moments before we were to go through the inspection of our daily output.

The corporal approached Bieda's stack. The latter noticed his visitor from the corner of his eyes and pretended to work with greater industry.

"You there!" The little corporal pointed with his empty bottle in Bieda's direction. "Come here!" Bieda ran as ordered.

"You're a thief! A dirty, no good dog of a thief!" the little corporal shouted. And the more he shouted the more enraged he seemed. His face turned purple and he leaned heavily on the stack of wood. The orderly stack of logs tumbled to the ground, rolling one over the other. Confused, Bieda attempted to speak.

"But, sir, corporal . . ."

"You're a son of a whore, a dirty, thieving son of a whore," the enraged corporal interrupted Bieda's stammering. "One who steals from a fellow prisoner ought to be taught a good lesson."

"What did I . . . ?" Bieda had no chance to continue. The corporal wobbled toward him, landing a hard blow at Bieda's head. Although he partially missed the target, Bieda lay prostrate in the cold snow, guarding his head in his arms, in anticipation of another blow.

I pitied him as he lay there trembling, with the drunk corporal upon him. At that moment I felt no ill-will toward the thief. I even understood why he kept my jacket, and I could no longer resent his concern over his own survival.

The corporal took hold of the jacket collar and as he pulled it upward, Bieda raised both arms to release it. As the little corporal walked away with the jacket, he called out to me and I followed.

In the midst of the snow-covered pine forest we conducted the most peculiar transaction. I cut open the hem of the leather collar. The money was there; five American dollars. As agreed, I handed the corporal my last savings. With it went my remote hope of buying my freedom. Perhaps it was just as well this way. My immediate need was good health. To anticipate a future I had better survive first. I marveled at the matter-of-factness of our transaction—there were no complaints; there was no haggling. There was only one dissatisfied party, the jacket thief Kazimir Bieda.

Our quota grew larger each passing day. Those of us

who had never before used the saw and the axe as tools of labor compared their blisters at nightfall. We had never supposed blisters would grow within blisters. They did. The food rations decreased when the quota was not filled.

Each night the work was checked and the shortages of one day automatically became an added burden for the next. Some among us could not even dream of accomplishing the labor they "owed" if they were to live another lifetime. They were kept on a bare minimum of rations for as long as they were able to work. When their usefulness terminated, they failed to show up in the barracks after a day's work. We all knew that they would not need to fill another quota ever again.

The days continued relentlessly. The little corporal drank religiously and waited for his prey. Each time I looked his way, his small, bloodshot eyes above the red, drunkard's nose were directed at my precious leather jacket. He had the money, but he wanted the merchandise also.

We kept on working. The Prophet worked as hard as he could and we all pitched in to help bring his quota up to the required standard. He was unable to keep up on his own. One of the guards cut off the old man's beard with a dull bayonet. It was a beautiful beard. It hurt but the Prophet did not cry out. We looked on helplessly. The sentry claimed it was a handicap at work. The Prophet took it philosophically. He was always ready with aphorisms. "It will grow back," he said, "as long as there is a chin to hold its roots." We all knew that. The beard would grow back. In due time it would be long and beautiful again. But as it would grow, our hatred would grow with it—a hatred and a will to live . . . a will to outlive our tormentors. I prayed. We all prayed together, and we worked together. The little corporal waited. He waited a week longer. At that time the monthly quota would have to be made up.

The week ended. I knew it even without the aid of a calendar: the last day of the week, the last chance to meet the quota. The little corporal kept on trotting around. We were thankful that the American dollars could buy an abundant supply of vodka.

A large bird flew overhead and came to rest on one of the pine branches. A shot rang out. A dead bird fell to the snow-covered ground, its frail body shattered by a bullet. The corporal kept on laughing with the laughter of a drunk. "One bird dead . . . , another dead soon," he jested, caressing his rifle.

It was sundown in the pine forest, a beautiful sundown. But we did not have the time to see the sundown. We worked feverishly and we prayed. Never before had I been so close to God. The little corporal inspected the day's work. We stood silently in ranks. The logs were neatly stacked. But there were not enough stacks to satisfy the monthly demand. The men stood mute. There was a triumphant glitter in the little corporal's eyes. His eyes caught mine.

"Let's go!" he ordered.

We marched. Neatly, like the logs, in columns of four we marched back to the camp. Not a word was said. Not a sigh was heard. We understood. We prayed.

Morning arrived. Everything was the same as usual except for the breakfast that was not served. Missing a meal could prove fatal to a starving man. Our shrunken stomachs asked for nourishment more persistently than ever. We stood the usual formation. The little corporal and his underlings approached.

"You!" the corporal addressed me. "Come with me!"

We went in the direction of a small wooden house. As we were walking away I caught a subdued "poor bastard," uttered by one of the men. I knew he wasn't referring to the corporal. We marched toward the house of the camp com-

77

mandant, the principal god. There all orders originated and all quotas were jealously accounted for. There, also, judgment awaited all "delinquent" prisoners. One did not enter the house and leave it through the same front entrance. There was a back way, leading into a secluded yard, surrounded by a tall stone wall. Tall enough, they said, to conceal the tragedy of those who were unfortunate enough to be judged by the mysterious chief god.

The little corporal knocked respectfully. A rather pleasant voice asked us to enter. There were no sentries. To my amazement, the commandant had the aspect of an ordinary man. A folder lay opened on the desk in front of him. I let my head droop between my shoulders as I stood before my judge and master. The little corporal was at my side. I had a foreboding of things to come.

"I see from your group record that you have not changed," the commandant's voice was as cold as the Siberian wind. "You have practiced sabotage and you continue." His manners were mild but firm. Men like this commit homicide joyfully. He made a short pause.

"Your honor," I started, but the little corporal motioned me to discontinue.

"They sent you here because you did not fulfill your obligations. You are delinquent again. We are concerned."

I stood listening silently.

"Sabotage is a serious offense nowadays, you know?" he said. His voice expressed the quality of genuine concern.

"I have a wife and children, sir," I pleaded, despite the reprimanding gestures from the corporal, "and I have a right to live!" I practically shouted in desperation.

"Our courts are just," the commandant said, as he clenched his fingers on the table in front of me until his knuckles were white. He did not look at me, but I knew that he had human emotions after all.

"You will be tried," he continued; "*if* you are found

guilty you will be given at least five years of hard labor. You have been stealing from the people . . ."

Tears came into my eyes. They bit like acid, yet they were sweet to the taste as they rolled into the corners of my mouth. I trembled with fear. I did not understand what the commandant was driving at. I knew that they were *all* thieves, one stealing from the other, all of them stealing from the government. The higher their position the larger their take.

"The law calls for the punishment of all saboteurs," the commandant's voice broke into my thoughts. "It is severe—severe but just!"

"Sir, all I ask for is another chance to make up for the lag," I pleaded, "only one more chance!"

"You have had your chance and you bungled it." He showed no mercy. "The law is clearly defined in these cases," the commandant said. He leaned back to pick up an impressive-looking volume. He leafed through it with a purposeful deliberation. He stopped. "Ah, here it is," he read, ". . . a fine of not less than fifty rubles is to be levied against common thieves." He stopped to study my reaction.

Fifty rubles? The corporal had taken my very last. I glanced at the last thing of value I possessed: the leather jacket. I would gladly part with it now. I did not dare suggest the jacket instead of the demanded fine.

The commandant studied the effect of his words. He stood up from behind his desk. The corporal was ordered from the room. The commandant approached me. He put his arm confidingly on my shoulder.

"Tell you what," he said. "Let me see that jacket for a moment."

I handed the jacket to him with a heavy heart. The commandant fingered swiftly the heavy places of the hems and pockets. He was an expert in the discovery of hidden wealth. But there were no hidden treasures left.

He tried on my jacket. Only the other day I had recovered it from certain loss. It was to keep me warm and healthy. The jacket was a perfect fit. The commandant seemed pleased.

"Get out, and don't let me see your face here again!" The commandant barked an order. The matter was closed as far as he was concerned.

Orders must be obeyed. They were invented for that purpose only. I obeyed. As I walked out into the freezing outdoors, I felt the sharp pain of frost biting into my exposed arms and the almost naked upper half of my body. There was nothing to guard me from the penetrating cold. I despised the little corporal for being the cause of my loss. The little corporal hated his superior for reasons similar to mine. But the commandant was pleased. He had no cause for hating anyone.

I walked slowly toward the barracks and I recalled the Prophet's aphorisms. But they no longer mattered. My leather jacket was gone irrevocably.

In all this misfortune I remain a Jew. Once more I am in need of a consoling thought. I chuckle when my comrades inquire cynically about my jacket. "I rid myself of the lice!" I tell them, but I do not believe this myself. And when I lay on my straw-sack alone in the silence of the night, my thoughts return to you, my beloved wife and children. I am happy to be exposed to the cold again. I am grateful to be alive . . .

Think of me, always, no matter what . . . as I think of you, with love.

Your husband . . . your father,
Henry

⮜⭃⮞ VOLKSDEUTSCHE

And seven women shall take hold
of one man in that day, saying:
"We will eat our own bread, and
wear our own apparel; only let us
be called by thy name; take thou
away our reproach."
ISAIAH 4: 1

When mother finished reading, we sobbed with her. Mother only uttered, "Thank God your father is alive!"

Work in the glass factory at Hortensia continued. The heat made a man forget the fear of Hell.

By now all Jewish property was almost entirely confiscated. The Lithuanian guards and their SS superiors entered the ghetto shops, took whatever they desired, and left without paying. The shopkeepers, although frightened at the goings-on, frequently chuckled after the enemy visitation, "Well, at least they left a little for the next ransacking! And they forgot to give me a beating."

The looting continued for some time. The commandant issued an order forbidding soldiers to enter Jewish shops without special permission. Yet the plundering continued. Jewish homes were spared at first, but early one morning the

Lithuanians swooped down on us. They called it "legal" confiscation of "enemy" goods. I feared a fatal outburst on Grandfather's part, but evidently even Srulko had gotten accustomed to the heavy boots. If he hated, he did not demonstrate it. Quite the contrary, he was jovial as he carried his cherished property onto the waiting truck. He made humorous remarks in Yiddish about the ignorant hirelings. But they were quite systematic and not at all ignorant about their task. They went from house to house and claimed whatever they could find. Their loot ranged from bedrooms and dining rooms to dismantled lavatories.

Things might have continued in their customary way but for Isaac the Gabah. Rumor had it that when the plundering Lithuanians entered Isaac's store, shouts for help were heard. The noise subsided as abruptly as it had begun and neighbors found the old templekeeper crouched in the corner of the store, the handle of a butcher knife protruding from his chest. He sat in a puddle of blood. The temple lost a faithful servant. We lost a good friend. Subsequently the Judenrat complained to the authorities. "The Bureau would investigate and punish the culprits," they were told. To think that only a few days earlier the old man lost his upper bridge during a beating he suffered at the hands of a band of Hitler Jugend. His despair about the inability to chew was common knowledge. "At least he won't have to worry about a new set of teeth," Grandfather said.

The hopelessness of the situation touched off a series of suicides. Isaac's son Shlomo swore to avenge his father's murder. He was frequently seen in company with some young people who were not at all the Hasidic types. "No good will come of it, I tell you," Grandfather said to us, "he'll only get himself in trouble."

There were peaceful days in the ghetto, too, although only sporadic. When they occurred, the people behind the barbed wire regarded the enemy as their benefactors. We were grateful for the smallest of mercies. But the peace was always of short duration. We heard rumors about camps where thousands of Jews were exterminated. One at Auschwitz in Silesia, another in Treblinka. And no matter how persistent the rumors, strengthened by occasional escaped witnesses, the people refused to believe.

Several weeks had elapsed. Roman and I worked diligently at the glass factory. We made good progress, increasing our skills and gaining the "respect" of our superiors. We were particularly pleased to have merited the friendship of our supervisor, Herr Edelmann. He was a kind man, and reminded me of Unteroffizier Boost. To sustain us in our efforts, he often smuggled food from the cafeteria and called us into his office under various pretexts to let us enjoy his contributions without arousing the suspicion of our fellow workers. Our brothers, the Poles, despised us because our employment threatened to deprive them of their inherited livelihood. We were fortunate to have a few overseers who did their best to ease our situation.

Even Herr Forster seemed more amiable than in the past. Upon seeing our column of ghetto laborers enter the factory gates, he would spit in his palms, rub them together, then grin his own inimitable grin.

"Work Jews," he told us, "or we will use you for soap!"

Indeed we had heard that the enemy's scientific progress was most impressive. No resource was to be wasted, organic as well as inorganic, alive or dead.

The persistent rumors ultimately had a frightening and most depressing effect on the ghetto population. Each day we were subjected to increasing abuse and humiliation. We were dependent on the whims of a world which no longer recognized the value of human life and dignity. And yet our work became more precious to us, because we realized that our very lives depended on our usefulness in the enemy's scheme of conquest. We began to labor under "delusions of reprieve," believing that conditions could not grow worse.

Of the many Poles working at Hortensia, I befriended one Tadzik Bosiacki, whom I had met during the days in the mikvah. It was he who had told me of strange happenings. But since non-Jews were forbidden by the enemy's decree to associate with the inferior people, we could talk only in the most subdued fashion.

As we were leaving the assembly line one day, he whispered, "I want to talk to you during the break. Something important has come up. Meet me at the usual place."

I had been waiting only a few minutes behind the great furnace when Tadzik emerged out of the surrounding darkness, but my anxiety made it seem much longer.

"I want to tell you all this myself," he began, "before others do, because I want you to know that not everything you'll hear will fit the truth."

"Go on, I'm listening," I said.

He hesitated a moment, as though trying to find the most appropriate way to explain things.

"Well, you see," he continued, "we are going to become Germans. The whole family, all of us will be Volksdeutsche!" Without meeting my eyes, he spoke quickly.

A painful pause followed.

"How can you become German when we all know your family to have a Polish background for many generations? Besides, why would you want to do that?"

"Everything is changing, Wilek. I want you to know that it is not only our family. There are many who will take the oath and become Volksdeutsche come next week." He paused for a moment. "And what's more, they are going to change the street names too! And we must learn German in school from now on, not Polish."

"But . . . but, how did all this happen?"

"The office of the Gauleiter notified the Railroad Commission yesterday. They told the supervisor that everyone employed in key positions would have to be of German nationality. You know, Father is chief engineer, don't you?"

"Well, yes . . ."

"So, you see, his is a key position and he must not only become Volksdeutsche, but he will have to belong to the NSDAP also." Tadzik maintained the apologetic tone of voice. I wondered how long it would take to make him feel at home with arrogance.

Realizing that the enemy had begun to woo the Poles, I knew that his interests must have taken a turn for the worse. The order had come from the German Military Governor Frank in Krakow. The enemy wished to recover elements of mixed blood and speech among the Poles whom he felt he had lost in the settlement of 1919.

Many categories of Volksdeutsche were set up. Some were regarded as safe and loyal, others were installed on a probatory basis. Various inducements were offered to win over as large a proportion of the Polish population for the second-class citizenship of the Third Reich as possible.

The goyim have been peculiarly discriminative and prejudicial, even toward one another, yet they were all united in their truculent hatred and persistent persecution of the Jews. The most vociferous by far were the peasants. I recalled Grandfather's claim that in actuality the Jews were a "blessing" to the goyim. He used to say, "Why, had it not been for the Jews' peculiar persistence and endurance in the Goluth, had they heeded the many cries of their enemies to 'go to Palestine,' the goyim would have been at each other's throats constantly."

All this passed through my mind as Tadzik remained silent. My contemplation was interrupted by the sound of steps. Suddenly Herr Forster emerged near our hideout. We held our breath for fear that any sound might betray us.

Soon after his arrival on the scene, we saw a shapely female figure approach him silently but in haste. They stood whispering for a moment, and we were sufficiently near to catch a word here and there.

"You come with me right now," Forster urged hoarsely, holding her hand in his. Her back was turned to us and we could not tell at first who the girl was, nor could we hear her voice well enough to recognize her. But Herr Forster's urgency explained much of her whispering. His voice rose, "No, I say you must come this moment, Bronia, do you understand?" She tried to wriggle out of his hold, and she turned her face toward us in her struggle. It was Bronia Kotek.

"Wait till her father hears of this," Tadzik whispered in a hissing voice, "the bitch!"

Suddenly I remembered what the men were saying about Bronia Kotek; about her "asking for it." I had not quite understood what she was "asking for," but I recognized that Bronia was a very pretty eighteen-year-old girl. She was herself well aware of this. In fact, she was the flirt of the glass factory, and seemed pleased with the effect she had on men. She dressed for the role. The flimsy transparency of her dress was evident in the daylight as well as against the bright flames of the great furnace in the factory.

As if on purpose, Bronia had no use for the protection of undergarments, and her shapely figure was vividly exposed when she walked across the yard. She was an assistant inspector of glassware.

Old and young alike desired her. Small wonder that Herr Forster had ample opportunity to observe, and develop an appetite for the plump flesh. One day at the factory gates he singled her out.

"Say, beautiful, we must see to it that you be placed on a better job than the one you hold."

"Perhaps we will, Herr Forster," she replied with a giggle. He followed her as she kept on walking. She drew her long pony-tail over her shoulder with a sharp movement of her arm. Her breasts heaved with the motion. "Some other time, Herr Forster, some other time," she dared to dismiss the chief god.

But Herr Forster was not one to be discouraged easily.

"It's good to have a friend in the proper position who can help when the time comes."

"I'm sure it is," she replied without glancing at him. "I'll remember that."

She intended to rejoin her party, but Herr Forster held her arm firmly. He addressed her with deliberate slowness.

"You must come sooner, Liebchen." He spoke to her now in German, the language of authority, of the superior who could not tolerate disobedience. It was his right to take what he desired. The chief god had spoken.

That incident took place scarcely a few days ago. I might have surely forgotten all about it were it not for our precarious position.

There were large wooden crates for carrying glass stacked throughout the darkened area surrounding the great furnace. Tadzik and I customarily met between two such crates. Herr Forster shoved Bronia closer to the crates near us, seeking the proper place for his designs. She followed without a word of protest.

"What is going on, Tadzik?"

"Shut up, Wilek, you want them to hear you?"

The girl fought quietly but desperately against his searching, strong fingers. Herr Forster held her tightly with one arm around her slim waist. With the other, he bent her over backward till she was prostrate on top of the crate. The crate squeaked treacherously under the weight, and Bronia continued in her attempt to escape from under Herr Forster's massive frame. Within the next few moments, in the quivering light of the furnace we observed the most mystifying proceedings. "Please, Herr Forster, please let me go." Herr Forster was too preoccupied to hear the clatter of our feet as we ran.

"To *him* she sold herself! The whore! She had it coming to her!"

We separated before I could say a word. After all, it was not as simple as Tadzik put it. I wanted to shout that Bronia was forced into physical submission. His family had accepted it willingly. I wondered how many faces life would let me see before I was to reach manhood.

A new order came to us from the desk of Governor Frank in Krakow. The Jews were forbidden to grow earlocks and beards. They were also forbidden to wear fringed garments. To the Hasidim this was a major defeat. Their very life was threatened.

Grandfather seldom left the house from then on. Grandmother would not permit it for fear he would run into "law enforcers."

"They'll have to kill me to take my beard," he repeated obstinately.

"Father, the Lord will not think any the less of you if you comply with the Gauleiter's orders and stay alive," Mother retorted.

"The Lord, blessed be His name, is merciful. He even forgives the converts, but does that mean that I must become one?"

He kept his earlocks, wore fringed garments, and remained home. So did many of the Hasidim for the time being. I missed their daily learned discussions, for they feared to congregate.

We had never realized how many "genuine" Deutsche had lived among us. Suddenly the town was full of them. Groups prowled through the ghetto, looking for earlocked Jews. These erstwhile Polish youths wore black uniforms with swastika bands and daggers attached to fancy belts with the ominous "H.J." carved on ornate ivory grips. One such group was about to amuse itself at the expense of a bearded victim, as I approached from a distance on my way home from the afternoon shift at the factory.

"Come here, Jude!" they shouted at a Hasid who must have left his apartment by necessity. "Don't you know the law?"

I came closer and, to my terror, I recognized Nora's Uncle Max. This was one of our own! I saw some of his tormentors. There was Heniek Popielski, whose "cultured" name was Heinrich Aschengruber. Adam Niski, now Adolf Klein, and Piotrek Kowalski, Peter Schmidt. They stood around Uncle Max with drawn daggers.

Heniek was the oldest and the strongest. He also was their leader. They all shouted and kicked the defenseless Hasid as he knelt before them. They pulled and pinched his beard and tore his earlocks on both sides of his temples. His entire face was soon covered with blood from his fractured nose.

"Heniek! Stop it, Heniek! This is my uncle you're beating!"

The gang was startled by my attempt to disrupt a cultural event. But the beating subsided for the moment. Heinrich, surprised by his "Christian" name, did not forget the days at the fence of the old castle on Ulica Zamkowa, when the whole lot of his gang had come to beg for scraps.

"Let him go!" Heinrich Aschengruber spoke with the voice of authority and self-confidence. Released, Uncle Max ran. He was running from Sodom, and there was no looking back.

"Why must you act this way, Heniek?" I asked, when we stood alone.

"The law is the law," Heinrich replied, "and no one can change that."

"But you don't have to enforce it, do you?"

"We are the law now, Wilek. . . . I am now where I belong, with my Vaterland, and I must do all I can to make myself worthy of this honor." We both knew the abyss of our separation.

"This time I remembered you, Wilek, and I repaid you in full. From now on you are not to address me in public. If our paths should cross again, it will be as German and Jew; I shall treat you accordingly."

I told myself over and over again that this could not be true. I tried to talk but no sound would come out. The event took place on the Adolf Hitler Strasse, which not long before had been Ulica Pilsudskiego.

"I leave you now, Jude, you must obey if you value your life. Heil Hitler!" He shouted the world-shattering salute, turned around smartly on his heel, and left me standing there aghast and hurt.

At home, I received a hero's welcome. Everyone was on hand to celebrate my "bravery." Nora's was the most welcome demonstration of gratitude.

In the midst of the enemy, beneath the swastika, the ancient amulet for long life, good fortune, and luck, which was now the symbol of evil, we found that nothing could lessen the pleasure of a slight squeeze of a hand, a kiss, and a fond embrace or a simple smile. Love's protective wings rendered us immune to the realities of the day. We remembered the words of Thornton Wilder: "There is a land of the living and a land of the dead and the bridge is love, the only survival, the only meaning."

And it came to pass . . .

*Enraged, for he was rendered
Helpless by the might of
Æsir's wrath, Loki disguised*

His evil face under the mask
Of cunning . . .

    And the sages cried warning . . .

To the unsuspecting gods,
As they, at Odin's wish,
Bid welcome in their midst
To one who was their mortal
Foe . . .

    And there was cause
    To bewail the tragic error . . .

✥ YOM KIPPUR MASSACRE

*Every one that is found shall
  be thrust through;
And every one that is caught
  shall fall by the sword.
Their babes also shall be dashed
  in pieces before their eyes;
Their houses shall be spoiled,
And their wives ravished.*
ISAIAH 13:15–16

The death rate was appalling. The dead were neatly stacked on the sidewalks and then collected in trucks which made regular rounds. We grew calloused to the toll. Typhus, aided by enemy harassment, as well as other infectious ills, spread death from door to door. Even though the Jews ritually observed cleanliness, the congestion made it almost impossible to avoid contagion.

Seemingly there remained only two types of inhabitants in the ghetto: those already emaciated in body and spirit, and others well on their way. Unofficially, however, there was also a third class, and as long as their wealth lasted they enjoyed the taste of good food and exemption from forced labor.

Although we had grown accustomed to death, we were nevertheless shocked to be personally involved in the business of fighting it. Apparently Max Mandel did not altogether recover from the Hitler Jugend beating. Only occasionally did he get up to participate in a minyan, gathered to assist a mourner. This he could not refuse. He was no longer a jovial, witty man, and it was increasingly difficult to stay out of his way. And then it finally happened. Max Mandel came down with a fever.

Small wonder that he became one of the many to succumb. In addition to the starvation diet, we lived without heat, water, plumbing, or the customary disinfecting materials, such as soap, drugs, linen, and enough clothing for frequent change. There was also a scarcity of hospitals, bathing establishments, and laundries. The number of physicians and medical personnel had been depleted because of the enemy's frequent arrests of the intelligentsia. That the epidemics did not grow to the proportions of the plague, cholera, black death, and other pestilences may be ascribed to the Jewish people's struggle against the infectious diseases.

But Mandel's illness once again drove home the tragedy of the ghetto. Nora lived with his ravings and slept only when they subsided. She managed to conceal her weariness in her prayer. "It is the will of the Almighty. It is the will of the Almighty, blessed be He."

Even when Max Mandel gave up his tormented spirit, Grandfather kept on stubbornly repeating, "God's will be done, blessed be He." Amid sobs and lamentations, services were held. The Kaddish was chanted by the hozon. And the gloomy cloud grew over the ghetto.

Then there was the matter of depositing Mandel's body as far away from our home as possible. The Gauleiter threatened to evacuate entire residential areas as soon as one typhus case was found, and he was a man of his "dejudaizing" word. He was the regional ambassador of the Führer's supreme authority and an example of the virile, highly refined Kultur of a superior people.

The Jews prayed fervently for salvation. They prayed

with trust in God's intervention. But there was no salvation in view. The ghetto guards were on constant rampage. Rape and murder were daily occurrences. Jewish women were continually rounded up under pretexts of being taken to forced labor. Brought to SS quarters, they were compelled to dance in the nude for the amusement of their inebriated tormentors. Many who were then sexually molested consequently committed suicide.

It was three o'clock in the morning when our burial party ventured into the empty ghetto streets. There were ten men to form the minyan. Several women joined the procession, silently weeping. Nora stayed home with Mother. The men took turns carrying the body, wrapped in sackcloth, two at a time. Weak from fatigue, hunger, and tension, it was a superhuman effort. The procession seemed to move one step forward and two steps back. The mournful bearers were near exhaustion when they finally arrived at the old cemetery on the outskirts of the ghetto. Were it not for its grotesque appearance, the scene would have surely assumed sinister dimensions. I carried two boards which were intended by ancient law and tradition to become the resting abode of the deceased Jew.

Grandfather officiated at the burial. He came from a long line of Cohanim. As a titular priest he had the authority to perform rabbinical tasks, but he did not quite know how to address the last farewell to one of his own. There was nothing to disturb the somber proceedings except the distant, occasional rattle of a gun and the regularly revolving spotlights. But as we stood praying, we were constantly alert to the noise of footsteps. Burying the dead without license was prohibited.

Moments after the body was lowered, two Lithuanian guards appeared.

"Halt!"

"Jude!"

"Jude!"

Shots resounded. The women wept hysterically and the men raised their voices in prayer.

"You'd better pray to us, you filthy scum!" one of the guards shouted. "Your God is on vacation."

"We haven't done anything," Grandfather pleaded. "Please let us go." A rifle butt silenced him.

"What have you hidden in the ground? Dig, you swine! You've buried all your gold and diamonds and you think you can fool us!"

It was useless trying to persuade the inebriated guards, and the men picked up their shovels. As they dug into the fresh ground, distant thoughts of resistance occurred to them. Ten against two. But every Hasid kept praying for his own salvation and they all continued to dig.

The moon faintly illumined the area and the guards slowly became aware of the women huddled together on the ground. One guard ordered them to line up and led the two most "appealing" away to the guardhouse. Ten against one. As though reading our minds, the remaining guard backed away a few yards. Suddenly wielding his shovel, one of our men lunged. A second followed. It took the guard only a few seconds to recover control.

"You filthy Jewish bastards!"

A short salvo and the two men lay on the ground. Some of us did not run fast enough. Grandfather fell.

"Go child . . . run . . . I won't last long . . . there is nothing you can do . . ." He coughed blood.

"I'll get you home, Grandfather. Please don't, I'll get you home." I tried to lift him but could only cradle his head in my arms.

Srulko died and a part of me died too. The shooting subsided.

"Grandfather say something, speak to me," I kept repeating. Then, carefully, I let his body rest on the ground and ran as fast as I could. I wept loudly and carelessly.

Two of the minyan survivors arrived home ahead of me. The task of explaining fell to them. My appearance momentarily interrupted the lamentations. My clothing was torn to shreds; my face and hands bore Grandfather's blood.

"What happened?"

"Where were you?"

"Are you hurt?"

I told the story as well as I could. Srulko Malpo died on the battlefield, and he had always wanted to die in his own bed.

There were no Hasidic sessions from that day on. Their spirit seemed broken. I missed their comments on the Torah. Many questions were unanswered, and the High Holidays were approaching. Somehow it did not seem right to observe the festivities with Grandfather gone.

Through the grapevine we had learned of the arrival of Sturmbannführer Doerings at the Seventh Bureau. He was the new Kulturverwalter, cultural administrator of the ghetto. The Judenrat was summoned to Doerings' office and made to wait the usual amount of time, sufficient to melt anyone's will to resist or negotiate. However, when they were finally admitted to the Sturmbannführer's office they were hopeful—Doerings looked more like a schoolmaster than a Gestapo officer.

"Meine Herren," Doerings began, "I called you here to discuss certain pressing issues."

The Judenrat representatives were impressed. To Sturmbannführer Meier they were nothing but "pigs" and "swine," but Doerings called them "gentlemen." They had almost forgotten the sound of that word. They were also amazed at the tone and polish.

"Gentlemen, as the representative of the Third Reich, I am the Führer's emissary to this entire province." He turned toward the huge portrait, raised his right hand to the ceiling, and saluted his leader with a crisp "Heil Hitler!" The Jews looked on astonished. The "little schoolmaster" was not one to be trifled with.

"To make it short, and I like doing things this way," Doerings went on, rubbing his palms together, "I've been dispatched here to look into the sudden lag in tax moneys. It is felt in Berlin Headquarters that altogether too much time has elapsed since the last contingent of ghetto dues arrived. I am to correct this irregularity."

"What have they done with the goods delivered them regularly by the Judenrat?" Warszawski cried out plaintively, but he did not elaborate. The Jew was beside himself with anger but knew to control his emotions before the dignity of the Third Reich. It would serve no practical purpose to accuse one god before another. The Jew had to be practical. "I am sure this can be corrected."

"Not only *can* it be corrected, but it *must* be done quickly and efficiently. If I am not mistaken, gentlemen, your High Holidays are approaching, and taxes are to be submitted to this office before a permit for worship is obtained! Verstanden?"

"Jawohl, Herr Doerings!" Warszawski had learned to address the enemy properly. He had almost raised his arm in a spirited "Heil Hitler," but it might have sounded awkward for a bearded Hasid to praise the Führer. On second thought, the Jew contemplated, it might not be a bad idea to wish the Führer a healthy future. After all, there were millions of Jews cursing the black mustache each day in their prayers and it all seemed to have a contrary effect.

"We must have two hundred thousand zlotys by noon Thursday if you are to use the synagogue on Friday."

"Two hundred thousand zlotys!"

"Two hundred thousand zlotys is only fifty thousand Reichsmark. I realize that the previous quotas were somewhat less taxing, but then, after all, you have missed the last few payments. We feel justified in our desire to eliminate the debt as quickly as possible. Is that clear?"

Incredible as it all seemed, the shattering demand was clear. They were sick with fear, for they suddenly realized the implications of the enemy's request. They wanted to bargain but did not dare.

Doerings was consumed with ambition. As an expert for the Bureau in extortion, he had made a point of studying the habits of the Jews prior to his new assignment. He knew their meekness. He was also aware of their bargaining skills. He expected a counter-offer, but it never came.

"We will do our very best," Warszawski said.

"Only two hundred thousand zlotys will be satisfactory!" Doerings replied. "You may go now!"

The astronomical figure still ringing in their ears, the Council members left. In their desperation they had forgotten to inquire about the two women kidnapped on the night of the Mandel burial.

Doerings watched the men of the Judenrat as they slowly walked out of his office. I pondered on what had occurred within the Kommandantur walls, but what I could not really know was that when the last one of them disappeared from view, he joyfully slapped his thighs, proud of the manner in which he had dealt with the shrewd Jews. Indeed, his work had begun in a conscientious and efficient manner. He would take no nonsense from the ghetto rabble and his merits would soon attract a promotion. How happy his Annelore would be! Her Wolfgang a Standartenführer! And Bruno and Richard, they would inquire about the insignia on their father's uniform! Things would be different for all of them once he got through dealing with the ghetto problem.

At ten o'clock, on the morning preceding Rosh Hashanah, the phone rang in Warszawski's office at the

Piotrkow Jewish Community Council. He was the only Jew with the dubious privilege of a telephone. The penalty for this "convenience" was countless hours of worry and desperation, and the effect of the ringing sound was immediate. "Two hundred thousand zlotys," Warszawski thought with apathy. The amount collected by his militia was nowhere near the amount demanded by the enemy. But the Judenrat president was too tired to worry. He let the phone ring several times before he reached for the receiver, a cardinal sin in itself.

"Warszawski here." The sound of his voice betrayed his anxiety.

"You will report to the Kommandantur at two o'clock sharp this afternoon. You will bring the money with you! Understood?"

"I understand, sir," Warszawski spoke with a deliberate slowness, "I shall be there at the designated time, but I cannot bring the two hundred thousand zlotys."

"How is that? You cannot. You realize, of course, what that means?" The secretary shouted into the phone. Warszawski kept repeating, "Yes, sir, yes, sir," while the lesser god ranted on for several minutes.

"How much have you to submit?"

"I . . . we . . . well, we have about half of the demanded quota."

There was a short, calculated pause at the other end.

"Be here at two, pünktlich, and call me first—regulations you know."

"Jawohl!"

Distrustful of the Nazi's intentions, many Jews stayed away from Rosh Hashanah services. But Doerings kept his word and there were no incidents. We left Felusia at home with Nora and went to the synagogue. This was our first worship without Grandfather's guidance. It was a meaningful worship, though. There was much to pray for. We had heard much lately about liquidation movements in other communities.

"Oh, God, inscribe us in the Book of Life, and give us strength to meet our enemies."

"Hear, oh Israel, the Lord our God, the Lord is One!"

Three days after Rosh Hashanah the president of the Judenrat was once more summoned to appear at Headquarters. He faced Doerings at the assigned hour, after having been briefed by the secretary and thoroughly frisked by the sentry.

"I have summoned you today in a most urgent and delicate matter," the enemy began unceremoniously. "As you know, we have in Piotrkow a large garrison of young, healthy men who unfortunately suffer from lack of sexual relations. Occasionally they find relief with women of the streets. These meetings have resulted in many cases of venereal disease. We cannot tolerate this situation much longer. If we allow it to continue, our war effort in this theater of operations might suffer. You are therefore ordered by this office to submit a list of young women in your community suitable to form the beginning of what will someday become a home for convalescent soldiers."

"In other words," Warszawski dared to interrupt the Sturmbannführer, "you are delegating to me the responsibility for the organization of a common brothel?"

"I have not used the word *Bordell*," Doerings replied, "the interpretation was entirely yours."

"Are you serious, or do you intend to amuse yourself at my expense?" Warszawski asked, hoping the enemy might see the absurdity of his demand.

"Our task allows us no time for joking. You will come to this office on Saturday . . ."

"Please, not Saturday."

"Very well, then, on Monday at one o'clock sharp. You

will present me with a list of persons suitable for the task of entertaining our troops. You must not worry. The persons involved will be well taken care of. The home will be arranged quite comfortably and in keeping with strict sanitary procedures."

The enemy might have continued in his enthusiasm, but Warszawski interrupted. A sudden transformation was evident.

"You have imposed monetary taxation, and we have complied with your orders. You have blackmailed, robbed, and humiliated us in the worst manner. We tried to adjust to our suffering. But what you ask of us now is that a mother offer her daughter to you to be used as a common whore. I can tell you now, your order will not be carried out! You can destroy us all, but you cannot make of us accomplices in as shameful an act as this!" Warszawski shouted the last words at the enemy. It was contrary to regulations.

"You are taking it altogether too tragically, my good man," Doerings condescended to cordial familiarity. "After all, you are a man yourself and you can understand the needs of other men."

"We are a religious institution."

"Look into your Bible. It is filled with brothels."

"We have come a long way since Biblical days, Herr Sturmbannführer."

"Come now, be realistic," the enemy continued, "this is war, and in situations such as this all principles and theories die out. Well?"

"May I tell you something?"

"By all means."

"I shall not be here on Monday with the list you requested, not on Monday nor any other time," Warszawski said calmly.

"How dare you! You Semitic imbecile, do you realize what will happen to all of you for this?" Doerings shouted at the top of his voice. Somewhat calmer, he continued, "Think of your people, think of yourself. It is only a question of time."

"Time is the commodity we seem to have much of. To us it is immaterial and irrelevant," Warszawski went on, "but it may run out on you, Herr Sturmbannführer. It has been our experience to wait, but you are ambitious. You have not learned to have patience. After all, our existence antedates that of the 'Thousand Year Reich' . . ."

Doerings rose abruptly. "Be here on Monday at one o'clock with the list, you filthy swine. And no more discussion!"

Warszawski left with mixed emotions. The Jew had won a moral victory. He had been able to reduce the enemy from "gentleman" to "swine" in a matter of eight days.

It was exasperating attempting to outguess the Gestapo. Even though Doerings' order was ignored by the Judenrat, there had been no repercussions.

The ancient house of worship was filled to capacity for Yom Kippur. Roman and I had worked the nightshift and we stayed at home to rest and catch up on our sleep, as usual. Grandmother went to the services with the neighbors. Mother, Felusia, and Nora remained at home.

An aura of peace and holiness suffused the ghetto. The late morning services were well on their way. One could feel all that was good and holy—love, affection, mercy, and worship—on this holiest of all holy days. This day His children's supplications are said to be dearer and more acceptable to the Almighty, blessed be He. And through the silence, the trilling voice of the great hozon meant to please the congregation and find favor with their Father in Heaven.

A rumbling noise awakened us. We hurried to the windows. A long column of trucks and armored cars advanced along Zamkowa in the direction of the Great Synagogue.

Each was filled to capacity with troops. On top were mounted machine guns, manned by Lithuanian SS.

It was almost time for Yiskor, the special services for the departed. Children below confirmation age would be let out of the sanctuary, since they were not permitted to witness the solemn occasion. It was too late for warnings. The rumbling had stopped. Sturmbannführer Meier barked a few short orders. In the next few moments the house of worship was completely surrounded. Still, the Jews were unaware. Incendiary bombs exploded inside and the SS sealed off the doors.

Frightened and confused, three hundred people pressed against the doors. Women and children screamed hysterically. The enemy guns sounded. Heavy dark smoke rose to the sky and the fire was in full bloom. Worshipers threw themselves out of the second-story windows. Many were killed by sharpshooting SS before they hit the pavement. A group of HJ sang the Horst-Wessel song accompanied by the garrison band.

Warszawski, dressed in his praying shawl, appeared in one of the high windows. In one arm he held a small boy, in the other the Torah. Only his lips were moving. The SS must have thought he looked comical, because they paused for a moment to laugh at the old man. A shot resounded and the old Jew swayed but leaned heavily on the window frame, refusing to come down.

Warszawski wrapped the child in his praying shawl. He looked down at Doerings and Meier. The flames were behind him. With the greatest effort, he heaved the child onto the ground below. It was his grandchild, the only son of his eldest daughter; a challenge for the marksmen. The small body lay motionless where it fell. Moments later the window collapsed and Warszawski fell back into the flaming structure.

Within a few hours only smoldering ruins were left of the Piotrkover Great Synagogue. Not one person succeeded in getting out alive. Yom Kippur had become for them Yom Hadin, "the day of Final Judgment." Some of the SS who turned away were ordered to witness the spectacle as a trial of their courage and devotion. Others took pictures.

When the trucks had gone and the ghetto returned to its mournful quiet we wept no more.

෫ఁ౾ఁ

And it came to pass . . .

Edda's children, the Thralls, were
Innocent as the children of Afi and Amma;
The Churls. Then Jarl was born, the first
Of free men, son of Fathir and Mothir, his parents . . .

And the sages grieve for the innocent
Victims of god's quarrel with god . . .

Behold, and see
If there be any pain like unto
my pain,
Which is done unto me,
Wherewith the LORD hath afflicted
me . . .
The youth and the old man lie
On the ground in the streets;
My virgins and my young men
Are fallen by the sword;
Thou hast slain them in the day
of Thine anger;
Thou hast slaughtered unsparingly.
LAMENTATIONS 1:12, 2:21

The events of Yom Kippur would be inscribed henceforth in the annals of Israel's afflictions, worthy of mourning
on every Tisha B'av. The Judenrat was dissolved. Warszawski was dead. The council authority was subsequently dele-
gated to the ghetto militia and its able head, Joel Katzman.
He was made of that special fiber necessary in the make-
up of a Gestapo lackey. Indefatigable in the pursuit of duty,
he realized what it took to safeguard his own interests, and
did not hesitate to betray his people and his principles.

Orders came down from the Führer himself and were
considered sacred. Needless to say, they were modified and

expanded by numerous officials before reaching Katzman, but he was not one to question their logic or origin. At times, he even invented a few of his own to earn the Bureau's praise. Like his masters, he wore a pair of shiny boots made by Uncle Moritz and carried a pigskin whip. When preoccupied with a forthcoming assignment, he would whip the side of his boots with a passion.

Roman and I continued as the family's providers and Nora would soon begin work at the factory. Forced labor had become an ironic necessity for ghetto inhabitants. The special Meldekarte, work pass, provided security for its holders. We were anxious to have Mother protect herself in this way, but Felusia was under age and Mother refused to abandon her. Even Uncle Moritz, once again reconciled to the family after the death of our Grandparents and Max Mandel, could do nothing to change her mind.

Meanwhile, long barracks were being erected at the far end of the glass factory yards. The preparations were disquieting, and within two weeks they were ready and furnished. Miles of barbed wire were wound around the entire work area and a dispensary and disinfection center was installed. Things were organized according to regulations.

Preparations to face the future more realistically were made secretly in the ruins of the old military headquarters on Polna Street. As an unprecedented gesture of solidarity among the Jews, the Hashomer Hatzair [the leftist Youth organization] met with the Mizrahi [Hasidic, or religiously oriented youth group] to devise a plan of resistance. Felix Rabinowicz led the militant Hatzair; Shlomo headed the Mizrahi.

About one hundred young men and women gathered in the modern catacombs. "No death without a fight!" They were going to sell their lives dearly.

"We must not face the enemy's schemes unprepared, we will not live in constant fear of death, our lives cannot be dependent upon the whim of a mercenary guard, a Nazi lackey, or a paid informer. This is serious. We are not playing games any longer," Felix continued. "The intentions of our masters should be obvious even to the most optimistic among us."

"What if we should increase their wrath by resisting?" one of the Hasids asked.

"You are free to withdraw right now. We will not hold it against you if you leave us. We ask only that you breathe nothing of these proceedings to anyone."

"Maybe if we do not resist they will leave us be."

"You may go on deceiving yourselves, but I prefer to face death consciously. I do not mean to play a hero. But, I ask you, haven't we reached the very lowest point in our existence?"

"We might be worse off if we challenged the enemy."

"The time of merely talking is over," Felix hissed. "You've talked a lot in the past; your complacency does not fit the times."

They listened and agreed. Someone had to take the initiative away from the enemy. Felix nodded at Shlomo to come forward.

"We have made contact with the A.K. during the past three weeks," Shlomo began, "and the Home Army has promised to give us as much support as they can. We have already received a small shipment of weapons and ammunition. All will be distributed among those of you who are with us. Now is the time to get out for those who wish to do so. There will be no turning back."

They looked at one another. There were faces betraying fear. There were some who could not have been over Bar Mitzvah age. But none withdrew.

"So be it," Shlomo said, "you will all be contacted soon. Get back to your homes, and don't draw the enemy's attention. We don't want any of you to get caught now. The

Gestapo is everywhere. Go now, and God be with you, blessed be He."

When the Meldekarten had been issued to all workers, Katzman was summoned to the office of Sturmbannführer Meier.

"We shall install additional lights on the public square by the coming weekend. I want sentries on all streets leading to the square at three o'clock on Saturday morning. Understood?"

Katzman clicked the heels of his shiny boots together. "Jawohl, Herr Sturmbannführer!"

The militia and its commandant carried out the orders to the letter, and they were discreet. Yet despite all their secrecy, we huddled together in our homes harboring no illusions about the approaching events.

Shouts and cries woke us before dusk on Saturday. It was that bewitching moment when the moon claims the universe from the sun, scarcely leaving enough time for man to surmise that he stands alone. The enemy shouted through loudspeakers. "Abandon your homes! Everybody into the streets!"

As people lined the streets in front of their dwellings, truckloads of Lithuanian SS arrived. They took charge of the disorderly crowds, shoving, pushing, and sorting the old from the young. Mothers were separated from their infants and small children. The multitude was herded into the public square, which was as bright as daytime. The newly installed lights worked well. Vainly attempting to save themselves, people ran in all directions, only to be dragged back, if able-bodied, or shot.

"Leave your belongings in your homes, you shall come back to them soon." In a desperate attempt to do things as ordered, people ran back into their homes to leave their bundles, but there too they ran into rifle butts.

Mother carried an overnight bag in one hand and

clutched Felusia's hand in the other. An SS guard abruptly tore the bag from her hand, throwing its contents onto the pavement. Several cosmetic articles hit the ground and broke into small fragments. The guard laughed violently. "You won't need those, you Jewish bitch!" He shouted further vulgarities and Mother wept as she hurried us on.

Men, women, and children were hunted down in their homes. Cellars and attics were searched, shots came from everywhere. Only after arriving at Adolf Hitler Platz was the magnitude of the newest enemy enterprise clear. The combined SS and Gestapo high commands were there. At this unprecedented occasion the two competing service branches of the Führer's elite worked together. Meier and Doerings shouted orders, whipping people into orderly columns wherever necessary. Schirmeck, chief god, stood apart and directed the proceedings. A militia man intercepted us and pointed to Felusia.

"The child must go to the group on the left. The rest of you go to the right. Do you have your Meldekarten?" Roman, Nora, and I displayed the work passes. Felusia cried as she was being pulled to the side, and Mother refused to let go of her hand.

"You'll be better off without the kid," the militia man said. He tried to sound sympathetic but his words had no effect. Then he noticed a Lithuanian approaching and shouted, "Come now, woman, decide! One way or the other!" Mother released Felusia long enough to embrace us.

"Be brave, my darlings. Don't worry. We'll be fine."

"Don't cry, Mother, don't cry." We kissed them.

"Nora, my sweet girl," Mother cried as she was led away with her child, "be well, my dear, God bless all of you!" Mother and Felusia joined and disappeared into the moving mass of the aged and the very young.

"We must go," Nora sobbed as she led us to the opposite side of the square.

A woman holding a small child in her arms ran up to Sturmbannführer Doerings. "Please, I will work, I will do anything you say, save my child." A guard ran to her with his whip. Doerings stopped him.

"You have a choice, woman," the Sturmbannführer said, "you can go to the right and live, or you can choose to go with the others."

"But my child, kind sir, my little baby!"

"Schmeiss doch den Abfall weg!" Doerings shouted, "Throw away this trash, woman!" With that, he turned on his heel to walk away. The woman ran toward him. Her free hand held a long kitchen knife. The guard shouted and Doerings fell as he turned toward the lunging mother. His right hand reached mechanically for the gun in his hip holster, but he never needed to use it. With one blow of the guard's rifle butt the woman fell awkwardly to the pavement. Blow upon blow followed while, frightened and bewildered, the child sat next to its dying mother, who at first attempted to ward off the blows as best she could. She was dead within moments. The guard helped his superior to his feet.

"What do we do with the bastard?"

"Links, das geht links!" Doerings shouted, "To the left, it goes to the left." The guard dragged the crying orphan toward the mass on the left, where eager arms tried vainly to soothe the hysterical child. The Sturmbannführer busily brushed the dirt from his once spotless uniform. Regulations explicitly called for spotless attire in public.

There was Uncle Moritz, his wife, and our two cousins, Mendel, age four, and Hershel, age seven, all huddled together among the people to the left. We shouted at them. They saw us too. Uncle Moritz looked at us helplessly. They waved. We waved back at them.

"Poor Uncle Moritz," Nora said, "he has made a tough decision."

We knew then that there were no privileged among our people. Those who were useful were spared only for the duration of their usefulness.

I picked up the thread of Nora's thoughts, "He must have run out of soft calf hide."

Gestapo officials joined the retinue of guards. They separated the able-bodied from the weak with the aid of shepherd dogs. The trained animals were only half deities, charged with punishing those who dared delay the proceeding by a last embrace or a farewell message called out across the square. Growling furiously, they sprang at the slightest provocation. Their masters took photos of the performance. With the arrival of the dogs, only silent greetings were exchanged with friends and relatives.

Some six hundred people between the ages of twelve and forty-five stood to the right of the square. On the opposite side were the children, their parents, and elders. While some were being driven systematically toward the railroad station, others kept arriving on the square from all directions. It seemed an endless process. To facilitate deportation, the Gestapo had promised better living conditions and milder treatment in the working camp of their destination. But we had all heard a great deal about the new extermination camps at Treblinka and Majdanek.

People were loaded into the waiting freight cars. There was standing room only. Many refused to enter and died on the spot. Others, though reluctant at first, climbed into the boxcars unaided. Occasionally the less able were clubbed and kicked as they attempted to be inconspicuous.

The proceedings lasted all night. Many had joined the countless shadows beneath the ghetto skies. The sun returned but hid as the darkness of the shadows turned into rain. It was a sign of mourning for the living.

On one side of the square there was only a handful left

for deportation. The gods were pleased. In the shimmering lamplight, their polished heels clicked together. Arms raised high in the mysterious salute. "Heil Hitler!" "Sieg, heil!" Another day, and the gods withdrew to rest.

No sooner had the last of the deportation-bound disappeared when the Militia Commandant Joel Katzman shouted at the remaining laborers.

"Let's get going, a column of fours!"

Leaving the gates, we looked back. The ghetto was flames and smoke. We could hear sporadic shots and outcries, and understood that the cleaning-up detail was nearing its end. Piotrkow was Judenfrei. Grandfather's house was gone. Srulko, his favorite staircase on Zamkowa 20, the rubles he kept in his attic, and the Hasidic sessions, they were no more.

Hours later the freight train came rumbling by our new camp. We had hoped to catch a last glimpse of our people, but large boards were nailed to the doors and the minuscule windows. The moving prison cells spoke eloquently, passing slowly as though deliberately attempting to prolong our agony. Tiny faces of children looked through the cracks, bewildered and frightened. From time to time a name was called. An arm reached out for a last farewell.

"I feel sick to my stomach, Nora," I said, "I think I'm going to vomit."

"You must be strong, Wilek. Now, more than ever, you will have to rely on your own strength." She spoke soothingly, caressing my cheeks and wiping my tears. "We must stand here and look on; they might be in any one of the compartments. You would not want them to miss us. Would you?"

"They will never be back!" I kept repeating.

"You mustn't think that way, dear, you mustn't torment yourself." Nora could not give up. "Let's pray together, let's pray for a reunion."

"The only reunion we'll experience will be in the beyond, if there is a beyond!"

"Do not blaspheme, darling, God will punish us," Nora said patiently.

"If He does not hear our prayers, how then would He hear our curses? Is He not too severe, this God of ours?" I meant to discourage Nora but she was loving, patient, and understanding.

With the ghetto liquidated, and Piotrkow Judenfrei, the Seventh Bureau and its representatives returned to Headquarters in Lodz, the Golem became the supreme law in the camp. We had long suspected Herr Forster of being a Gestapo representative. With supreme authority left in his able trust, it became obvious. Only a small nucleus of SS guards remained. Katzman was the liaison between the inmates and Forster.

We spoke to factory foreman Edelmann, and Nora was given a relatively easy job in the sorting department. Edelmann was kinder than ever. He quickly procured a Meldekarte for Nora's little cousin Hayim. The boy came to work with us. After all, Roman and I were old hands at glassblowing by then and we were able to show the novice "the ropes." Even the Poles were kinder to us after the ghetto liquidation. There was no deliberate persecution. Some found it necessary to voice sympathy for our grief and it meant a great deal to know their loyalty could be bargained for.

Three months had gone by since the deportation. Things were mostly routine; we worked the usual three shifts; we listened to the news from the eastern front, desperately hoping for a Nazi defeat which did not want to come; and we were religiously ordered to the Entlausungshaus in weekly installments. Delousing was more rigidly observed than the feeding of the hard-working inmates. Rumor had it that the enemy feared he would be denied the pleasure of Juden-reinigung were we to succumb to illness brought on by lack of cleanliness. However, despite all precautionary measures, we found it necessary to spend a major portion of our free time searching for vermin in the seams of our clothing. At first one devoted one's attention to the delousing activity in privacy, embarrassed at being surprised by an unannounced comrade. As time went on, however, delousing became as commonplace as scavenging for food particles in the guard kitchen garbage cans.

After the ghetto had been burned down and the new dispensary at the work camp built, a physician in charge had to be selected as well as several assistants. Of the many applicants, Forster selected three finalists. Dr. Franz Gomberg was among them. The process of elimination was simple. Each was told to appear before his prospective "employer" with his spouse, if married. The interview was brief. The forthcoming duties were explained, along with the necessity of "contributing" to the commandant's fund. "This is all I possess," each of the aspiring physicians had said when delivering his contribution. Forster chuckled; Doerings had told him of the Jews' ability to conceal wealth and he thought of ways.

When Dr. Marek Jablonski entered Forster's office, followed by his wife Masha, the overseer almost committed the unforgivable blunder of rising before a Jewess. Her beauty was breathtaking.

Things followed their natural course. Dr. Marek Jablonski became Hortensia's chief physician, although his professional background was the least impressive due to his youth and inexperience. His assistants were Dr. Franz Gomberg and Josef Spiker.

Dr. Franz Gomberg had had the distinction of belonging to a people who considered themselves worthier than their traditional brethren; the indignant Herr Doktor was a half-breed. His Jewish-German physician father, Dr. Richard Gomberg, had married a Christian nurse, Hildegarde Ehre—despite the threats and pleadings of his parents. He was anxious to begin a new life, free of tradition and religious prejudices. Religion was on the way out and Richard was a modern man with new ideas. In time, he had sufficiently assimilated himself to forget his Jewish heritage. During World War I he had earned the highest honor his beloved Vaterland could bestow on her son, the Ritterkreuz I. Klasse. There was no limit to his privileges, including his country's solemn pledge to afford his first son free education to become Herr Doktor, like himself.

It was most natural for Franz to follow his father's example. He became a physician. He also renounced whatever traces of Judaism had been left in the Gomberg tradition.

Franz prospered. He had moved into the most exclusive neighborhood of Berlin and only the cream of the Berlin society gathered at his mansion. No one had ever accused Franz of lack of generosity. The Gombergs were Germans first and last.

Things went exceedingly well for Herr Doktor Franz Gomberg, as he was customarily called. So well that he had completely ignored the events of the early thirties. He had heard of the new leader but was not interested in the Führer's theories. He was a practical man involved in the pragmatic struggle for affluence. In fact, he rather admired the new leader for his dynamic personal manner and his ingenious methods of opening new avenues of income for his countrymen. He was particularly awed when the great Führer turned the defeat of 1918 into victory in 1938.

Gomberg had resisted at first when his old friend Erich Stellrecht, dressed in an S.A. uniform, issued him eviction papers. But his resistance lessened when he learned the reasons. In keeping with the Nuremberg decrees, no person of Jewish ancestry was permitted to own property within the boundaries and jurisdiction of the Third Reich. And according to the statutes, he, Herr Doktor Franz Gomberg, the son of a genuine bearer of the Ritterkreuz I. Klasse, was a Mischling ersten Grades, a half-Jew, unworthy of being considered even a low-class citizen of the glorious realm.

Gomberg's despair was great. He had felt the pain most acutely because of the suddenness of the denunciation and the irrevocability of his grotesque destiny. But his was not the deepest hurt. His wife Anna, a blonde, blue-eyed Aryan, had never given much thought to her husband's heritage. To her he was a good German, a true patriot. It took her weeks to adjust to the new role of a Jewish wife and mother of Mischlinge dritten Grades. Her children were one-eighth Jews. She was almost reconciled to the stigma when Heinz, her oldest son, became despondent upon his dismissal from the Realgymnasium and took an overdose of barbituates from his father's medicine cabinet. A few days later Anna was found bleeding to death in the family bathroom; both her wrists were slashed open. She was pronounced dead by her husband. A modest burial followed with only her Franz and the remaining two children present.

And when the Third Reich had acquired vast new areas of Lebensraum, the Judenfrage had advanced another step toward the "final solution." Thousands of German Jews were transported east, among them Mischlinge of an innumerable variety of degrees. Dr. Franz Gomberg was taken to the Piotrkow ghetto and subsequently to the Hortensia work camp. His two children were in different camps. Regulations called for *Familientrennung*, the separation of families.

It happened during the night shift rest period. We ran with the crowds in the direction of the screams. There stood Bronia Kotek vainly attempting to conceal her nudity. We were amazed to see the Golem's mistress in a most compromising situation. Her head was shaven clean; the absence of her once beautiful blonde hair made her grotesque. A small swastika clearly tattooed above her abdomen branded her a traitor to Poland. There were whispers and gasps around her, but the girl did not seem to notice. One of the workers threw his overcoat over Bronia's shoulders. She headed directly for Forster's home.

"How did they do it?"

"Who cares, she had it coming."

"It's the work of the Home Army."

"She is a traitor, isn't she?"

"Oh, leave her alone, you'd be glad to do what she did, if you were as beautiful!"

"Well, she isn't pretty now! Serves her right!"

Some of the assembled sympathized, and she even found defenders among the women. No one knew why Bronia came to the factory at that hour—she was exempt from work by Forster's orders—but it was rumored she came to meet her secret lover.

We were awakened earlier than usual on the following morning.

"Everybody out! Appellplatz!" The Golem's voice had the quality of special danger. Katzman struck nervously at his polished boots with his whip, and the entire militia stood by waiting orders.

"A grave crime has been committed in the plant last night!" Forster shouted. "A woman was violated. We must punish the guilty! Aid us in bringing the criminals to justice, and I promise you, you shall live to see your families!"

Our god spoke of justice and of crime, and he demanded punishment. But no one was eager to denounce the "criminals." For once, facing the Golem mute and defiant, we enjoyed the upper hand.

"The Golem will blow up any moment now," I said to Roman who stood next to me.

"I only hope he won't be too close when he does," Roman whispered.

Herr Forster did explode. Jumping up and down, shouting incoherently, he furiously lashed out into the frontmost ranks. The men desperately tried to avoid his blows. He then turned abruptly toward Joel Katzman, who stood at attention, his whip idle. The exchange was brief. Joel clicked his heels and answered "Jawohl!"

"I promised Herr Sturmbannführer to settle this matter between us," Katzman began, "and we must all share the responsibility together. Sooner or later I'll find out who was behind this barbaric deed. But we do not have time to waste. Things have to be done, and they have to be done fast. I ask your cooperation in helping me find the guilty party. You will be rewarded if you do. If you choose to remain defiant, reprisals will be taken against your deported families. You don't want that, do you?"

No one stepped forward.

"I am through playing games," he shouted at the silent ranks of men and women, "I'll get the people I want if I have to hold you here forever! No wonder the Germans hate you! You are nothing but swine! I will have you stand here until you fall from exhaustion!"

Three days and two nights we stood in formation. We were permitted only to go to our workshift and return when the factory whistle blew. Those who fell to the ground were clubbed all the way to the stockade at the far end of the camp. After three days Katzman announced that those jailed would be hostages for the guilty. If the culprits were not delivered in the next twenty-four hours, the hostages would die.

"From now on, you will stand at attention!" Katzman yelled, "Anyone who steps out of line . . ." He made an expressive sign.

The four of us were getting off the night shift when we

heard Katzman shouting and militia removing fallen inmates.

"I can't go on," Hayim said.

"You must," Nora answered with finality. "Look, there's Edelmann." Roman pointed, "What's the guard waving at us for?"

"There is a truck at Gate 2 waiting to be loaded with half-liter jars. Hurry up you four, I want it done now." Edelmann tried to sound as indifferent as circumstances permitted, but still it looked a bit awkward to have been selected for this choice assignment. We hesitated and he shouted angrily.

"Get moving! I said I wanted it done right now!"

Eagerly we ran toward our detail as Edelmann saluted the guard.

Of the thirty men and fifteen women tortured at the militia headquarters, eighteen "admitted" complicity with the A.K. Although each told a different story, they were quickly "tried" and sentenced to twenty days in solitary confinement. Katzman knew full well that a sentence as severe as that meant certain death, and he finally felt sure he had asserted his authority with the inmates.

On the third night a group of A.K. insurgents entered the militia headquarters. Two of Katzman's men stood guard at the door. They were quickly tied, gagged, and deposited on the floor of the stockade. Without attracting attention, the insurgents entered Katzman's quarters. He was awakened from his sleep rudely but did not utter a sound. He opened his eyes to face the menacing barrel of a submachine gun.

Everything happened rapidly. There was no time to plead. Katzman was gagged and forcibly led into the solitary. After having released the prisoners, Katzman was told to face the wall. One of the insurgents put a silencer on his Luger and Katzman fell bleeding from the side of the skull.

On the following day Katzman was found by one of his men. He was hanging by his ankle from a high ceiling lamp. On his back was the note:

DEATH TO THE TYRANT!
A. K.

And it came to pass . . .

Tyrants were born, in Loki's desperate
Bid for Æsir's supremacy.
Ramses, the great Pharaoh decreed,
*   And he said:*
"Destroy the first born, lest
All shall perish in retribution!"

And it came to pass . . .

Amalek and Abimelech, scheemed Æsir's
Doom, and they were followed by
Lesichon, king of Ærmoris, and Ulog,
King of Barshan, and Caesars came, and
Herod, and Haman serving the god of Hel . . .

And the sages wept . . .
And it came to pass . . .

For it was not an enemy that
*   taunted me,*
Then I could have borne it;
Neither was it mine adversary
*   that did magnify himself against me,*
Then I would have hid myself
*   from him.*
But it was thou, a man mine
*   equal,*
My companion, and my familiar
*   friend . . .*
PSALMS 55:13–14

The execution of Joel Katzman was as ill-timed as it was brilliant. Not only had it caught the Golem and the entire militia unaware, but it also indicated the overseer's inability to cope with the problems of discipline. Meier was recalled from Lodz. He arrived with a strong SS detachment, approximately forty men and twenty dogs. The camp braced itself.

Forster was the first victim of the purge. His case was pursued and solved. Before the week was over, he faced a panel of his peers, headed by Sturmbannführer Meier, the new supreme god. Although we suspected that we were to be next on Meier's list, it was a day of rejoicing in the camp.

The court came promptly to order. Meier leafed through some papers with deliberate slowness.

"You are well aware of the reasons for which you were

summoned to appear before us," he began, casually glancing at Forster. "The Bureau does not tolerate incompetence, Herr Heinrich Forster, not your kind of incompetence."

"But . . . Karl . . ." the Golem stammered.

"You will address this tribunal with the proper respect and detachment, Herr Forster!"

"Jawohl!" Forster replied curtly.

"You will speak when spoken to, verstanden?"

"Jawohl!"

"You must answer to this tribunal on two charges. Eins, you are accused of fraternization with the enemy of the Third Reich."

Forster was confused. Bronia would not have gone to the Gestapo to denounce him. He had repaid her many times over for her favors. Yet he could not be sure. He stood at attention listening to the indictment.

"The second charge is more serious than the first, it is incompetence in the line of duty. How do you plead to both charges?"

In his desperation, Forster decided to defy his peers.

"You are not serious, are you?" He chuckled nervously.

"The accused will limit his remarks to the matter at hand. I repeat, how does the accused plead to the indictment?"

"Not guilty, of course," Forster replied arrogantly.

Meier remained unperturbed. Forster was worried. It was that certain smile on Meier's face.

"The Bureau always suspected your sanity, Forster. You were all too ostentatious for your means and position," Meier went on. "After your latest exploits, however, your lunacy is no longer only suspected."

Forster listened in disbelief.

"The Bureau was alarmed at your incompetence as well as at your liberal behavior patterns concerning the Nuremberg Laws."

"But I never . . ."

"You never went to bed with a Jewess? That is exactly where you were completely duped. Only an idiot could have permitted that to happen."

Bronia a Jewess? No, it could not be! I would have known!

As though reading Forster's thoughts, Meier snapped his fingers together. The side door opened.

"Bronia Kotek . . ."

Had Meier not mentioned the name of his former mistress, Forster might not have recognized her. The swelling eyelids created two narrow slits. Her eyes pleaded mercy. She moved forward with extreme difficulty, stepping awkwardly sideways. Her lips were cut. There were no traces of nails left on her fingers.

"Bronia Kotek," Meier repeated, "do you know the man before you? If your answer is 'yes,' nod your head once. Do not make a sign otherwise."

Bronia opened her mouth instinctively but could make only inarticulate sounds. Forster realized her tongue had been extracted. She nodded once.

"This man, he was your lover. Yes?"

Another nod.

"Now listen carefully, Bronia, and reply as best you can." Meier spoke once again with a deliberate slowness. "Was your name originally Bejla Kotzelson? Do you hear? Kotzelson?"

She nodded again without visible emotion. The Sturmbannführer was pleased. He was ready.

"Bist du Jude?" Meier shouted at the tormented girl.

There was no reaction at first. Meier shouted, "Bist du Jude? Bist du Jude?" There was a nod, and the girl was dragged out of the room by the two guards. When they got her into the courtyard, the Gestapo performed one of its rare acts of mercy. An agent of the Seventh Bureau approached and the guards let go her arms. Bronia slumped to the cobble-stoned pavement. The Gestapo official put his Luger to Bronia's head. The impact of the bullet propelled her forward and she fell several feet away, half the contents of her skull scattered in all directions.

Forster heard the shot and knew Bronia was more fortunate than he. His trial had only begun.

"This tribunal shall reconvene tomorrow exactly at ten o'clock in the morning," Meier announced curtly. In accordance with regulations, the junior officers quickly rose to their feet. As if by a secret sign, they all faced the large portrait on the wall. Each raised his right arm and shouted a very formal "Heil Hitler!" Forster might have stood staring at the floor for some time, but the brisk salute of his former comrades startled him. He murmured an almost inperceptible "heil" and slowly walked out of the room.

Instead of covening as planned on the following morning, the Gestapo took its time. Forster was brought before his peers a week later. That was precisely the way of the Seventh Bureau. By slow degrees they would break resistance. By slow degrees Meier introduced his "third factor." Finally it was revealed,

"Heinrich Forster, du bist ein Mischling zweiten Grades!" ("You are a second-degree half-caste!")

Not only did Meier's terse statement shock the defendant, it also drove home the terrible injustice of this trial. Why was he being humiliated? He was neither the first nor the last Gestapo officer to commit a blunder. He was willing to share the blame for his inefficiencies. Why this sinister conspiracy to defame his honor? He, a descendant of proud Junkers, would never admit to the preposterous accusation that he belonged to an inferior bloodline.

Was it really Meier who thought up this queer scheme? Forster tried to piece fragments of events together. He had always suspected his close associate and immediate subordinate Hans Seemann of a silent envy. But he didn't think Seemann was sufficiently intelligent or cunning to have manipulated this intricate plot.

Could it have been that Jew-loving Edelmann? It was common knowledge that Edelmann aided many Jewish laborers. Yet each time Forster had accumulated sufficient evidence, he lacked the necessary witnesses. Even his informers refused to testify.

Forster could think of many men who should have been accused in his stead. Their sins against the Reich encompassed a far wider breach of duty than his insignificant involvement with a Polish harlot. Yes, he had been guilty of minor misdemeanors, but even the most conscientious Gestapo officials considered beating camp inmates unconscious as routine. And many times Forster had limited himself to merely kicking or whipping the workers to avoid injuries and production lags at the factory. For this he had earned the Reich's temporary gratitude.

He had accepted bribes, but hadn't he entertained his friends as lavishly as his gains permitted? As Forster looked around the courtroom his mind wandered and time seemed to slow down. He saw Doctor Franz Gomberg and wondered what he, an abominable Jew, conspirator against the Reich, was doing there.

Yet Forster felt relieved when Meier called Dr. Franz Gomberg to the stand. A favorable witness. Things would take a turn for the better.

Dr. Gomberg stood at attention. Only once did he glance at Forster.

"You are familiar with the accused."

"Yes, Sir."

"To what extent were you involved with him?" Meier continued.

Gomberg was uncertain about the implication of the last question. He hesitated for a moment.

"Come, come, speak up! It isn't all that difficult to make up one's mind about as simple a question as that!"

"The accused was my superior."

"In what capacity are you employed here at the camp?" Meier continued.

"I am a physician."

"In what manner were you selected for the position?"

Hot and cold sweat trickled slowly down Forster's athletic neck.

The doctor hesitated once more before replying. "I had paid a price for this privilege, Herr Sturmbannführer!"

"Why did you not report this to the Bureau previously?" Meier asked.

"I was afraid." Gomberg was telling the truth.

"Had the accused threatened you with punishment?"

"Not in so many words, but . . ."

"But what? Speak up, doctor, speak up!"

"Well, well . . ." Gomberg kept repeating the *also* and *nun*, which are part of the German language for the sole purpose of time consumption.

"I feared for my life," the doctor finally said. "Herr Forster was unscrupulous in his dealings with the inmates."

"How many physicians are there in the camp dispensary?" Meier inquired.

"Three, Sir."

"Are you the physician in charge?"

"No, Sir."

"Who is the chief physician?" Meier knew exactly how many persons were employed in the dispensary and who was in charge, but he detected a note of bitterness in Gomberg's replies and was determined to exploit it.

"Dr. Jablonski had been placed in charge of the dispensary by the accused," Gomberg replied.

"Do you approve of Herr Forster's choice?"

"It is not my right to question the decisions of my superiors, but to carry out their orders." Dr. Gomberg emphasized the words *Recht* and *Befehl* as only a German would have, and Meier knew to take advantage of the age-old patriarchal concepts.

"It is your duty to speak your mind," Meier warned, "this is a court of law."

"Forster was influenced in his choice," Gomberg blurted out impulsively, daring to delete his former superior's official title—a most un-German occurrence, contrary to regulations. Meier was only too glad to overlook the irregularity.

Forster's illusions were shattered. For the first time, the Golem realized that women were to be his undoing. His Grandfather Friedrich Forster had predicted it after Heinrich had raped his first victim, a thirteen-year-old hired farm hand. Heinrich was only fourteen. When the War for Lebensraum was started, Heinrich's peers happily volunteered his services to the Reich, for he had been involved in several lawsuits brought against him by the estranged husbands of seduced ladies.

When the opportunity arose for Heinrich to become commandant of a forced labor camp, his Junker family felt it was a godsend. However, he soon established the reputation of a rogue among the women workers. His favored expression, "Liebchen, komm' mit," had become as familiar to the factory women as their native tongue. Some were unable to withstand the temptation to better their lot. Others yielded to the overseer's persuasive talents. All were relentlessly abandoned as soon as he saw a fresher victim.

For Masha, the beautiful wife of Dr. Jablonski, Golem had broken all precedents. Her husband had been made head of the medical staff despite his inexperience and lack of funds. The young couple had been assigned special quarters adjacent to the dispensary, a privacy never before afforded a Jewish family. And during the weeks preceding his trial, Forster neglected the general factory inspections in favor of Jablonski's quarters.

There had naturally been a great deal of talk concerning Forster's clandestine visits with Masha. Much of the rumble reached Dr. Jablonski, but he was not one to interfere. He was not eager to jeopardize his and his wife's safety and was silent despite the immeasurable pain which he felt each time he accidentally miscalculated the overseer's visitation period. It was one thing to hear but quite another to meet the chief god on the threshold of his bedroom and find his own Masha lounging in the nude on their bed.

Forster frantically searched his mind to find a law, a precedent in the intricate jurisprudence of the Reich, which could help him. His memory was filled with regulations on camp administration. Suddenly he realized that Meier had engineered a highly irregular trial for personal gains. The testimony of Jews and Mischlinge had been presented against him. The evidence of scum. He shouted with all the passion of his past glory:

"You cannot condemn a Junker of ancient Germanic blood before this lowly court! You will not dare!"

Meier observed the apoplectic Golem calmly. He took time to jot down several notes.

"Heinrich Forster, your impudence is appalling, but typical of your kind." Meier rose slowly. "You are quite correct in stating that this tribunal could not condemn a true Junker. Quite to the contrary, the Junkers are the pride of the Reich. But you, Heinrich Forster, are not a Junker. Your shameful deportment is a dishonor to their great heritage. Your incompetence is unworthy of the Reich, your behavior comparable to that of an inferior race. You are tried before this tribunal not as a misguided son of our glorious Reich, but as a Mischling Zweiten Grades!"

And even during the last moments of his life, goose-stepping toward the gallows in the middle of the Appellplatz, flanked by erstwhile comrades, he was unable to understand. The noose tightened around his athletic neck and his distorted body hung on display for a total of seventy-two hours. Large signs were attached to his chest and back.

ICH BIN MISCHLING ZWEITEN GRADES

And it came to pass . . .

Treacherous and cunning are
The disciples of Hel, even as Loki,
Their master supreme of trickery and
Deception, quarrel together in soul-perishing hate . . .

And it came to pass . . .

Paris begets agony and fiery death
For the sake of a woman; and Brutus slays
Caesar, his friend, only to perish
Himself in agonizing pain . . .

And it came to pass . . .

The gods spin the fate of
Mortals, and many come and go,
With vengeance in their souls
And anguish in their hearts . . .

And the gods remain without sorrow . . .
Only the sages mourn mankind's fate . . .

. . . Behold and see
If there be any pain like unto
*   my pain,*
Which is done unto me,
Wherewith the Lord hath
*   afflicted me . . .*
. . . The Lord hath set at nought
All my mighty men in the midst
*   of me . . .*
. . . The Lord hath trodden as in a
*   winepress*
The virgin daughter of Judah . . .
. . . The youth and the old man lie
On the ground in the streets;
My virgins and my young men
Are fallen by the sword;
Thou hast slain them in the day
*   of Thine anger;*
Thou hast slaughtered unsparingly . . .
LAMENTATIONS 1:12, 15; 2:21

Even though the people had chuckled about the peculiar
fate of their former overseer, the camp braced itself for reprisals. Meier was promoted to Obersturmbannführer and
Herr Hans Seemann became the new Lagerkommandant.
With the typical zeal of a newly promoted official trying to

please another newly promoted official, Seemann intended to restore discipline and order in the camp.

To offset the anticipated Gestapo purge, the Home Army acted swiftly. Their primary target was Obersturmbannführer Meier. The A.K. met on Saturday after midnight, late in March of 1942, in Block 4. Some came from other barracks, and some took short leaves from the night shift. Everyone was present, including Felix, Shlomo, and Franek Zagrzebski, head of the A.K. in Piotrkow. Zagrzebski was on the Gestapo's wanted list and his courage and presence of mind served us all as an example. Nora insisted on coming. She had been meeting Felix for some time, and I feared that she and her clandestine lover might constitute a danger to the organization. But she pleaded time and again during the night shift, and I gave way—partly because her constant presence at my post might arouse suspicion.

We were startled to see Edelmann at the meeting. Although we had suspected all along that his sympathies were on our side, we had never dreamed he would be one of us. He smiled. There were no questions. Zagrzebski opened the meeting.

"We were told that the enemy is preparing another bloodbath." He glanced toward Edelmann and we knew the source of his information. "We've got to strike first at the Gestapo to break its intentions, and quick!"

"We're listening," Felix interjected. "What's the plan?"

"To insure the success of our operation, we must capture Meier. We know that he visits a certain Mme. Wiasnowa on Himmlerstrasse 13 religiously each Sunday afternoon. He remains there till the late hours of the night. He is driven to and from the house in his convertible Mercedes by his trusted bodyguard, Hugo. Hugo the ape. He must be killed before we can get to Meier."

Three men were selected. Josef Gabnik, a glassblower,

Jan Kublon, the "giant," and Zbyszek Zawada, a machinist. They were all experienced. The forthcoming Sunday, an important NSDAP holiday, was selected as the time for the abduction.

"We know how they love their festivities," Zagrzebski concluded, "and we only hope that they will observe the forthcoming festivity with more enthusiasm than all of the previous occasions. Every distraction on their part will aid us in our undertaking."

An "all clear" was given by the men on the lookout and silently Block 4 returned to normal.

I was about to sneak back into the plant when I heard a scuffle and distinct sounds of voices in the yard. "Verfluchtes Schweinehund!" followed by the pleading of two women, and a man's voice urging, "run, darling, run!" I recognized the voices of Felix and Nora. On their way back, they had stumbled upon an off-duty Lithuanian SS and his girl, about to indulge in their usual recreation. Both women ran, but Felix was apprehended and led to the guardhouse. When I got to Kublon with the news, he put his huge hand on my shoulder. "Felix must take care of himself for now. There is nothing we can do at this time. The plan must succeed. Get back to work."

Although I had no affection for Felix, I feared for his safety. I resented Nora's affection for him, because it lessened the strength of our own relationship, yet the success of our operation depended upon his endurance, and I wished him luck for the Gestapo was persuasive.

The following week was a busy one for the Home Army. The sounds of explosions and fire were commonplace. The Bureau called in reinforcements from Lodz—special SS forces headed by Doerings. But, as Zagrzebski had foreseen, they were helpless against the hit-and-run tactics of the A.K. For the first time since Nazi occupation, the Gestapo was on the receiving end.

Meier was insane with anger. Hostages were taken, beaten, and interrogated. No one talked. The Obersturm-bannführer was stymied, and fear of forfeiting the grace of his superiors took away his sleep. His most trusted informers were silent. All they were able to deliver was vague notion of "something in the making."

Meier lived in a large house surrounded by a wall and well guarded by SS troops. The three men assigned to his abduction observed his habits. When Sunday arrived they were ready. The Hortensia Partisan Organization was also prepared for armed resistance. They would carry out diversions and, if necessary, establish a common front with the A.K. in the forests.

As expected, march music blasted on Sunday through every radio in town. Music was followed by interminable speeches and more music. The A.K. was aided by the enemy's consistent lack of imagination; most of their actions that festive Sunday had all been accurately calculated by the insurgents. Late in the afternoon Wagnerian melodies were broadcast as a prelude to the main event—the Führer. They all listened attentively and, even though the Führer's address was its usual, hysterical, inarticulate ranting, there were endless shouts of "Sieg Heil" and "Heil der Führer!"

Afterward, the merriment and orgiastic celebrations commenced in all SS quarters.

With fatal punctuality Meier's Mercedes arrived at Himmlerstrasse 13. Meier gave his trusted adjutant last instructions. In good spirits and whistling a complicated Wagnerian tune, he entered the house. Moments later, Josef and Jan came around the corner singing a merry military march. They wore SS uniforms and did not arouse Hugo's suspicion. At a yard's distance, however, Hugo saw the determined expressions and opened his mouth to shout a warning. Jan fired his sten gun and Hugo fell to the pavement.

Meier had reached Mme. Wiasnowa's apartment when he

had heard the shots but there was no time to react. Before he could let himself inside, Zbyszek jerked open the door and pointed a Luger at his belly. Meier was allowed only sufficient time to follow meekly the orders of his abductors. Mme. Wiasnowa, gagged and bound to the bedpost, was left to the mercy of future investigations. There was no reason to fear that she would escape the unique Gestapo justice, for they were sure to reason her into the conspiracy against their agent, and Zbyszek's orders were not to waste costly ammunition on her.

Once on the street, Meier realized the magnitude of the happening. Hugo's huge body lay grotesquely sprawled on the pavement in a puddle of blood. The motor of the Mercedes was running, and Meier was urged into the back seat by Zbyszek's gun. In the car, the Gestapo officer was knocked on the head with a hard object. Before he lost consciousness, however, Meier noticed that both men wore SS uniforms.

The enemy was enraged by Hugo's death and Meier's disappearance. Forty thousand marks in all were offered for information leading to the culprits. Although that amounted to more than anyone in Piotrkow could even remotely dream of, no one came forth with the information. The strength of the Home Army dwelled with the people. And the people sanctioned its activities.

More hostages were taken from homes in town and a large number was selected at random from the camp barracks. Most town hostages were elderly men and women. Youth had gone into hiding. Prison walls resounded with shouts of pain and lamentations. Many died in the interrogations. Some were executed with their relatives looking on. But no one had spoken.

Then they brought in a new contingent of hostages. Nora was among them. They were marched through the prison gates into the yard. Suddenly, from one of the small cell windows above, her name was called loudly and desperately. The sound penetrated the monotonous shuffle of the prisoners' feet and drew the attention of the guards. Within the next hour both Nora and Felix had become objects of curiosity for the investigating Nazis.

"Get up, you swine!" A sudden splash of cold water splattered Meier's face. He almost choked, but without protesting got to his feet. The A.K. was quick to come to the point.

"The Bureau holds many innocent captives, Herr Meier. We want them released."

"Let me go, and they shall go free," Meier said without hesitation.

"Not so fast, mein Herr, not so fast. Your promises mean little to us. Besides, you are to be tried for your crimes. You have committed many, you know." Zagrzebski spoke with an emphasis calculated to break Meier's spirit. "Now you will listen, and you will obey!"

The enemy stood meekly before his former victims. The many years of patriarchal upbringing had had their effect. Germany had developed its tradition of subordination to the military point of view with the ascendency of Frederick the Great of Prussia. "Order, discipline, and work," were household words in Hitler's Germany. Defeat was only to be inflicted, never suffered. National Socialism worshiped the invincibility of the swastika. Because of it, the Nazi could do no wrong.

Now, the Führer's own Obersturmbannführer of the

elite guard found himself in a most awkward situation. The insurgents' menacing sten guns aided the Gestapo officer in learning his first lesson in humility.

The "court" was quick to reach its decision. In one voice the men responded "guilty!"

"You have been found guilty of crimes against your fellow men," Zagrzebski said. "Have you anything to say for yourself before I pronounce the court's verdict?"

Meier turned toward the court. "I am a soldier, I cannot question the orders of my superiors. Let me live, I beg you. I have a wife and three children in Mannheim. Let me live."

Zagrzebski smiled contemptuously and spat through his teeth.

"We know that you have always done a little more than you had been ordered to do, mein Herr, and we shall not delete all that from your good record. We will give due recognition to all your acts, merciful and otherwise."

Only then Meier realized that his doom had been sealed. True to his formal upbringing, he had never understood how to act kindly or mercifully toward his charges. He could not comprehend why the men who held him at their mercy found fault in the many selfless acts of his devotion to his Volk, his Reich, and his Führer. That was most puzzling to Meier.

"Surely, you are not about to condemn a man for doing his duty?" Meier inquired meekly. "Mine is an unblemished record."

The men deliberated briefly. "You shall live," Zagrzebski began, "but only if your life will guarantee the safety of the hostages who now are at the mercy of your henchmen."

A note was dispatched the following morning. Over Meier's signature was an order to release the hostages, and the A.K. waited for Doerings' reaction. His reply came the following day at sunrise with the public execution of ten hostages. Zagrzebski himself delivered the news. Moments later, not far from the A.K. hideout in the forest, Meier was told to dig a sizable trench. He dug until sundown; his tools were his own bleeding fingers. He was almost finished with his task when Gabnik and Kublon approached.

"Run, Nazi swine!" Kublon spat. "Run for your life!"

Meier ran, without direction. His bare feet were cut to shreds and his face was bruised by low-hanging branches. He was nearing exhaustion when he was cut down by the burst from Kublon's gun. A god lay dead, and the Valkyries laughed.

While the guards stood stunned, Meier's cadaver was thrown from the speeding Mercedes to the pavement in front of the SS Headquarters. The belated shots drew Doerings and his staff from the building.

"After them, you idiots! After them!" he shouted, enraged at the bewildered sentries. But everything had happened with incredible speed, and the insurgents were gone long before the SS set out in pursuit. Hours later the SS returned with the abandoned Mercedes. Its gasoline tank was empty.

Although he had died as a coward, the SS wanted to give Meier a god-like burial. The Obersturmbannführer had been slain in the line of duty. Goose-stepping ranks of his infuriated comrades, accompanied by the senseless but penetrating rhythm of the H.J. drums, paraded ahead of the coffin. Fellow gods followed the solemn procession with all the pomp and fanfare of their Teutonic ancestry. The Piotrkow population was ordered to witness the proceedings, which lasted the better part of a day. They were Doerings' insurance against another surprise appearance of the A.K.

A reign of Nazi terror followed Meier's assassination. Two hundred and eighty hostages awaited a miracle. But the

Home Army was silent. It had drawn large forces of choice SS troops from the Russian front to Piotrkow and considered its operation a success.

While the terror lasted, the SS had its enjoyment. Felix's desperate cry had given the SS a novel idea. All young women were separated from the remainder of the prisoners, ordered to disrobe in the prison yard, and forced to dance to Wagnerian music for the amusement of the assembled officers, wives, and concubines. Lithuanian guards were ordered to join the "dance," ultimately selecting their victims and carrying them off. The women who resisted were brutally beaten on the spot. Some were chased to the far corner of the yard and drowned in the prison well. The music played and the spectators were delighted.

Finally Felix, with his haggard face close to the steel bars, shouted at the top of his voice:

"Murderers! Stop it! I'll talk! I'll tell you all you wish to know!"

All merriment stopped. The women were led back to the general prison hall. No single cells were available. There was silence among the hostages. It was the silence of defeat; one of them had yielded. It had all been in vain.

Soon after, Felix was brought into the prison hall. He talked well, and was permitted to spend his final hours with Nora. They embraced and none dared to rebuke the lovers for claiming the last breath of life. None dared assume the harsh prerogative of judgment.

"They won't let us down. The A.K. will come to our aid," Nora said, caressing Felix's head. "They will free us, you'll see."

"No, I don't want it. I don't know whether I could be free again," Felix sobbed.

"Are you trying to fool God, Felix?"

"What God? There is no God!" he replied.

"Don't blaspheme, my darling," she continued soothingly, "everything follows a higher order, what must be, must be, we must have faith."

"Faith is the evidence not seen. It is overshadowed by a ruthless reality from which there is no escape." He spoke sobbingly, without the courage to meet her eyes.

Nora prayed.

"Whatever happens, dearest, don't allow anyone to rob you of your faith. It is the fortress of your existence," he said and he kissed both her eyes.

Aided by Felix's confession, the efficient Gestapo machine went into frantic activity to crush the A.K. But none of the identified insurgents could be found. The infuriated enemy took further hostages, increasing the total of prisoners to three hundred and forty. Doerings issued his ultimatum. Bulletins were posted throughout the area:

> THE INSURGENTS MUST LAY DOWN THEIR ARMS
> AND PUT A STOP TO ALL RESISTANCE. THEY
> MUST PLACE THEMSELVES AT THE MERCY OF
> THE GESTAPO, OR THE HOSTAGES WILL BE SHOT
> WITHIN THE NEXT FORTY-EIGHT HOURS.

During the following two days I worked mechanically, daydreaming about a timely rescue. At night I had fantastic dreams about smashed-in heads and severed limbs running in all directions. Everyone was tense and ready. But deep down, there recurred the feeling that if we did not antagonize the enemy, he might give us life.

Forty-eight hours after Doerings' announcement, the prisoners were herded into the awaiting trucks and the motorcade moved slowly through the empty streets of our shtetl. Only an occasional movement of a curtain betrayed onlookers. There were no incidents; no protests. Mournful prayers, beneath the gray canvas covering the trucks.

They came to a halt at a clearing several kilometers beyond the outskirts of the town where an immense trench, four feet deep, had been previously dug. Three machine guns were placed in position before the order was given to unload the truck. Men, women, and children stood quietly regarding the preparations in disbelief. Only a handful of guards facing three hundred and forty condemned. Doerings spoke.

"This is your last chance to save yourselves! Help yourself and live! Tell us where we can find the A.K. Don't you see that no one cares what happens to you? Do you think I wish to have you shot? Step forward and stay alive!"

A woman ran toward the speaker. "Take my boy, please, take him for your own; I don't care what happens to me, only save my boy!"

"Speak, woman! Speak and you both go free!"

"There is nothing I can tell, I know nothing of the A.K." It was the truth. "See how beautiful my boy is? He will look handsome in a uniform. Take him!"

Doerings gave a sign. A husky guard took the child from her and pushed her back into the ranks. Moments later the boy lay at her feet, thrown there by the guard who had plunged his bayonet into the child's body. Berserk with pain, the hysterical mother assaulted the assassin, only to be similarly dealt with.

"My men are not assassins! But they will do their duty! Speak up, I say, or no prayer will help you!" Doerings shouted furiously at the top of his lungs.

In unison they prayed, Christian and Jew, each to his own God; they prayed fervently in the spirit of Easter and Passover, for forgiveness. They prayed even as they were ordered to place their clothing in neat stacks by the graveside. Disrobed, they stepped into their common grave, many clinging to each other. Their prayers became faster, more desperate, and totally incoherent. But there were no miracles.

"Feuer!"

Doerings' command came suddenly even though it was expected. Felix managed to place himself in front of Nora as a protective shield. With the first burst they fell to the ground, his bullet-ridden body covering hers. When the firing finally ceased, only a few groans came from the moving mass of flesh. These were silenced with skillful pistol shots administered by the inspecting Doerings. He was quite pleased with himself. In the morning he would report to his superiors in Berlin. He had ordered his unit photographers to stand by, and they had been quite busy. He would enclose the photos in his personal file. They would come to good use.

The SS detachment made a triumphant return through the deserted streets of Piotrkow several hours later. Thirty men were dispatched to cover the grave. They had specific orders to recover belongings—nothing was to be wasted in the Third Reich.

During the brief absence of witnesses, Nora emerged from her grave. She had suffered shock and numerous bruises. Felix was dead at her feet. Not a sound came from the others. She gradually realized that her life was miraculously hers. In her stupor, she climbed over the edge of the grave and ran toward the forest. She stumbled over hedges and wild growths, but ran again to the safety of the trees. There she collapsed.

Yanek Brama, the young forester, had gotten up that dawn to get ready for his customary inspection of the district. His dogs were restless and the barking and howling caught Yanek's attention. He hurried out of the lodge and released the animals.

For ten minutes Yanek followed the sound of the barks. Suddenly it stopped. He called out to the dogs but they did not come. "I'll teach you a lesson, wait till I get hold of you, you ugly beasts!" he mumbled to himself. When he had reached the clearing, he saw Nora and was quick to put the events together; the distant salvos of the firing squad, the girl's blood-spattered body.

Yanek threw his jacket over Nora's nude body, not without admiring her natural beauty. Carrying the feverish girl to his lodge, he placed her gently on his bed and carefully washed her entire body, caressing with the soft sponge the most intimate objects of his dormant desires.

Three days and three nights Nora lay delirious. Yanek had not left her bedside for one moment. He knew the common symptoms of pneumonia and he attended to her as best he could. He learned a great deal about his unusual charge as she relived experiences countless times in her delirium.

On the third day, the fever broke. "Where am I? Who are you?" she inquired faintly. Mechanically, her hands clutched the cover above her breast. She attempted to raise her head from the pillow but it dropped back helplessly.

"You must lie still, Nora," he said, and she wondered how it was that he had called her by name.

"I know all about you; you have been very ill, with high fever," he continued. "You are safe here. I am the forester in charge of this area. No one will look for you here, and if they come, my dogs will warn us." Then he introduced himself, almost too formally for the prevailing circumstances. He smiled, noticing her embarrassment and the protective attitude she had assumed. "There were things I had to do," he said apologetically, "I hope you understand. You were quite a sight when my dogs found you."

Nora silently gave thanks to the Almighty. She realized she was at the mercy of the stranger, but once again she found strength in her deep trust in the Maker, blessed be He.

Her youth and an unbounded desire to live coupled to bring about a recovery. After several days she was still weak but able to get out of bed and attend to limited house chores. She dressed in some garments provided by her benefactor from his own wardrobe. Although her past experiences had taught her costly lessons about men, Yanek had given her no reason to suspect malevolent intent. He went about his work in daylight, and when night came they would chat about the war and related things.

"It's time for me to go into town for supplies," Yanek announced on the morning which marked the end of Nora's second week in the cabin. "Usually, I would not have gone until next week, but there are two mouths to feed now, and we will be out of provisions if I don't attend to it immediately."

"What . . . if . . ."

"Don't worry, you'll be fine; I'll leave my dogs. They know you now and will obey. I should be back late in the afternoon. If the dogs should warn you, run north. There is a cave nearby where you can hide. I'll look for you there if you're not here on my return."

He left with a short "bye," and somehow the fear of the persecuted returned to her soul. Every innocent noise of the forest alarmed her. The whistling of the wind in the trees announced danger; every cracking of dried-out branches meant enemy footsteps.

Nora sighed with relief at the friendly bark of the dogs late that afternoon and went outside to greet Yanek.

"What did you hear in town? How are the people at the factory?"

"The camp is still there. There have been no further incidents, but there is talk about an impending evacuation . . . the Gestapo is looking for an escaped foreman. Someone named Edelmann, and there is also a price on Franek Zagrzebski, the A.K. leader. A substantial reward has been posted for all fugitives," he added without looking in Nora's direction.

Nora wept. She was worried about her cousin Hayim, and felt guilty because he was still exposed to hunger and the trials of imprisonment.

They walked into the hut and Nora helped place the provisions in the cupboard. On the very bottom of one of the boxes she discovered a half-liter bottle of vodka. Yanek jerked it out of her hand. Surprised, but too preoccupied with Hayim to worry about her host's behavior, Nora went about her work as usual.

That night when the drunken forester found her, though she hid in the darkest corner of the hut, she prayed.

"Gotenyu, mayn tayrer Gotenyu. My dearest, darling God, help me now, please, dear God, help me!"

"Come here Jewess, come here this instant!"

Yanek tossed the empty bottle into the fireplace. It shattered into small fragments with a sound reminiscent of raids and bombings. Nora scarcely had the strength to remain upright after that.

"Must you do that?" she asked meekly, pointing at the bits of glass which had burst into every corner of the room. "And just after I had tidied it up a bit. It's not like you to behave this way."

"There are many things you don't know about me, my little dove," Yanek replied mockingly, "but you will learn sooner than you think."

"You must go to sleep now, Yanek, you are tired, and you won't be able to get up for work tomorrow." She tried to sound firm and concerned at the same time. She remembered from somewhere that firmness was the proper attitude toward drunks.

"Come to me!" He moved with great effort. "You and I, Jewess. I liberated you, didn't I?"

Nora pulled abruptly away and Yanek lost his balance.

144

Infuriated, he rose to his feet, more rapidly than could be expected from his condition.

"You filthy bitch! You Jewish swine! How dare you refuse me!" She tried to evade the blows. "For some fancy SS officer you would undress, wouldn't you? But I am not good enough for you?!"

"Please have mercy, I am still a bit weak. I am not up to what you ask of me. Perhaps later on. Please. O God, dear God, have mercy!"

"Didn't I liberate you? Didn't I risk my life to nurse you back to health? Where is your gratitude?" he kept repeating as he tore the garments he had provided only days earlier.

For a few short moments Nora was able to defend herself, as she kicked, twisted, and scratched. She bit his neck but her resistance only made her more desirable.

"You should have left me where you had found me. You can never force me to love you. I cannot be grateful for this. Please let me go now. Perhaps later, when it is all over, I'll come to you voluntarily. I shall be grateful . . . you'll see . . . please . . ." He was, of course, too strong for her and the last thing she remembered before consciousness faded was his close animal face and the strong scent of alcohol.

When she awakened from her faint, it was morning. Completely disrobed, she lay on the floor next to the overturned table. The disorderly aspect of the room brought back vague memories. Then there was the pain. A pain which was not entirely physical; it was more the result of a gradual awareness that the long years of maternal tradition had been erased; she was no longer pure, no longer a maiden. Even if she survived the war, she was unable to envision a normal life for herself. She was like all the others, desecrated.

"God, O God, why this punishment? What have we done to displease You so? Gotenyu, Gotenyu, why have you turned from us?" She held her head in her hands and moaned, but there was no time for lamentations. As she regained composure, her first resolve was vengeance. Yanek was gone. She dressed quickly. Then instinct dictated escape, but where would she go? Yanek Brama's cabin was still the safest refuge for a fugitive.

Hours passed before Yanek returned. He looked disheveled and remorseful. Expecting the girl to greet him with violence and hatred, he was astonished that Nora went about her chores as though nothing had occurred.

White, blinding snow stretched from horizon to horizon. It was a typical Polish winter which forced all life into hibernation. Days became shorter and Yanek spent most of his time indoors. He went to town twice monthly for supplies. Only then, because of concern for Hayim, did Nora's persistent silence break.

On his last return from Piotrkow, Nora had detected a change in Yanek's behavior. They had lived together sufficiently long, under most intimate circumstances, to know. Something had gone wrong, but she feared that questioning might arouse his violent temper. Yanek had beaten her on occasions when he was drunk, or simply infuriated about her presence, and when winter came he drank frequently to "keep warm." Actually, he had never been able to overcome his initial shyness and feared that the resentful captive would refuse to submit.

"Your cousin Hayim escaped from the camp," he blurted out quickly upon entering the cabin.

"How did this happen? Where is he gone?"

"I don't know. All I know is that his name was on the list at the Kommandantur among other fugitives who had escaped only a few days ago."

"What else?"

"There is an even bigger price now posted for any information leading to the apprehension of escaped Jews." He stopped for a moment. "I was tempted."

Nora's heart beat violently. "Am I not worth more to you than the price offered by the Gestapo?" She tried to sound as sweet and alluring as the circumstances required.

He glanced at her for the first time since his return. "Let's not fool one another, my dear. Although you've had your good moments, we both know that you hate me as much as the Gestapo."

Nora was puzzled and alarmed by Yanek's attitude. She wondered whether his sudden indifference came as a result of her pregnancy. But how could he know.

"You must not betray me now!" she pleaded. "I have lived up to my bargain, haven't I? Haven't I?" she wept.

"I made no bargains with you, Nora. Besides, I am Volksdeutscher now, and I must think of my own future. But you would not understand that. All you can think of is yourself and that cousin of yours."

"What are you going to do? You can't denounce me to the Gestapo! You know what my fate will be! Yanek, I have been like a wife to you. I am . . ." She wanted to tell him about the child, but he laughed contemptuously and she was determined that nothing could make her accept him as the father. He tossed his new identity card on the table.

"Here, read it yourself."

His name was Johannes Tor, that much she surmised, and he was raised to the rank of an officer in the Heimwehr.

"I know that you must do your duty now," she said, returning the document to the forester. In a way, she was glad it was over. "They'll call you 'Hans' for short, you know."

"You don't understand, Nora, you will never understand. You are a wonderful woman, but you are a Jewess. There is no place in the Third Reich for you. I am truly sorry, but there is nothing else I can do."

"You can kill me right here yourself and spare me the Gestapo. You have done that much for an animal."

"I couldn't do that, Nora, I couldn't kill you in cold blood. After all, we have gone through a great deal together."

Two days later, Johannes Tor had led the Gestapo to the girl he had initiated into womanhood. His reward had been a five-pound sausage and a gallon of vodka; it was explained that the large sums of money offered were only meant to entice the enemies of the Reich—the inferior races. A true Volksdeutscher did not need rewards for duty.

Each day Nora was violated repeatedly by the interrogating Gestapo officials. It mattered little. In her unique way, she reasoned that Hayim was safe because she had paid for it with her own ordeal. But she did not allow herself to think that her God was as demanding as the enemy's gods. She fulfilled a function, although through the pain of her daily suffering she failed to distinguish precisely what that function was. The Gestapo suspected her of A.K. connections.

"Give me strength, dear God, and courage to face my days' end. Don't let me suffer much longer, Gotenyu, hear my supplication!" she prayed during the interminable "interrogations."

One month had elapsed from the day Nora was placed in her latest confinement. With little food and repeated ravishing by the guards, Nora, like the other girls, was near exhaustion.

It was Christmas eve when the guard led her into the interrogation chamber again. There was food and drink on the table and a festively decorated fir tree in the corner.

"Eat and drink and groom yourself a bit," she was ordered by the officer in charge. "Tonight there is no interrogation. Tonight you celebrate with us."

Nora believed this to be the last meal. "A pity," she thought, "it isn't even Easter." But her fears were dispersed when four women entered the room escorted by festively attired soldiers. A fifth SS man joined Nora at the table. She understood then the total implications of the event.

The evening progressed and the enemy became increasingly sentimental. Candles were lit and festive songs were sung until excessive alcohol obscured the mission of the holiday. An orgy ensued, during which the women lost count of the repeated violations. At first they faintly resisted, but after a point they remained motionless, inarticulately mumbling what sounded like a battery of prayers. Nora alone kept full awareness by repeating the names of her loved ones. When the Viking Gods had their fill, they vacated the premises, giving place to lesser officials who eagerly joined the festivities.

Slowly and yet somehow suddenly, Nora realized that there would be no end to the abuses. The enemy would come to her in a never-ending sequence. She broke away from the guard who stood bewildered, his hands holding his loosened trousers. Half-mad and crying, she took hold of a knife which lay nearby on the table and with a wild yell plunged it into the heart of her would-be master. He let go of his trousers and fell, grotesquely trying to shield himself from Nora's repeated blows.

Moments later they dragged Nora through the courtyard. Insults and blows mingled with the sounds of "O Tannenbaum, O Tannenbaum, wie treu sind deine Blätter." As they put a bullet through the back of her head, Nora had little awareness left of her surroundings. She hummed an age-old lullaby to her unborn child, and fell lifeless to the pavement. From one of the barred cell windows came the haunting melody of "Whither shall I go . . . ?"

◆◈◆

And it came to pass . . .

As in the days of old, the
Woman knocked, rejected, onto many doors,

Each time she looked around with care,
Lest evil eyes would spy her presence there.

    And it came to pass . . .

Good Gefjon's sad demise, the virgin goddess,
Whose gentle love the tragic spinsters gained,
Enraged the giants and the gods alike,
For it was woman, and from her womb came earth . . .

PART TWO

Hate and Faith

❧❦❧

And it came to pass . . .

Loki, the foe of the gods,
Consumed by the venom from
The serpent of hate, came forth
From the Gates of the Dead . . .

The sages proclaim . . .

He writhed in dreadful pain,
And he shouted and cursed,
And the earth did tremble,
And the Æsir took heed . . .

And it came to pass . . .

The doom of the gods was near,
And many a hero was slain.
And Odin, the father of Æsir's realm,
Summoned the forces of good

And he said:

"Come forth, brave knights and kings,
Prepare! And be of good cheer!
The wicked must perish! Slay them,
Even as they slew Balder, my son!"

And it came to pass . . .

In his wrath, Loki summoned
The forces of Hel before him.
And he conjured the Hel-hound Garm,
Turned eagle, as black as Loki's hate . . .

And he said:

"Circle the mount where hero Barbarossa
Dwells, and bid him come with us!"
And the hero of War descended, awakened
By the vengeful spirit of the swastika . . .

And the sages wept,
And the struggle began renewed . . .

*And it came to pass, when Israel
had made an end of slaying all the
inhabitants of Ai in the field,
even in the wilderness wherein they
pursued them, and they were all
fallen by the edge of the sword,
until they were consumed, that all
Israel returned unto Ai, and smote
it with the edge of the sword.*
JOSHUA 8:24

On the battlefield of Borodino, where Napoleon fought
the bloodiest of his battles on September 7, 1812, the invading
Nazi armies began the attack on Moscow in the middle of
October 1941. As they had 129 years earlier, the Russians
attempted to block the way to their "Holy Moscow" and, as
then, took up the battle with exorbitant tenacity. But the SS
troops gradually pushed the Russians back out of their forti-
fied positions of Mozhaysk.

The battle for Moscow was raging. It was possibly as
important as the one of 1812, but it was tougher, mightier,
and longer lasting. Its cruelty and disregard for human dignity would be inscribed in the ever-recurring history of war.

Joint units of the Fourth Panzergruppe, under the command of Colonel-General Hoepner, led the immense German
autumn offensive. They advanced persistently from the
Roslavl area. On the 7th of October, after a forced march of

over two hundred kilometers through Russian territory, its spearhead, the Tenth Panzer Division, met the Third Panzergruppe under the command of Colonel-General Hoth at Vyazma.

The gigantic encirclement of Timoshenko's armies was accomplished. The enemy was in his greatest glory.

The regiments Deutschland and Führer of the SS Division Reich attacked the combined Russian forces. They broke through the Moscow defense positions although the defenders fought desperately and bravely.

Soviet riflemen lay with fractured skulls in their foxholes, trenches, and bastions. Some sat over their bunker weapons, burnt to ashes. Many were strewn about, their stiff fingers over the stringers of their weapons. Others were slashed by Nazi artillery fire in rows and packs. Still thousands more were led away. At night one could hear the lamentations of the wounded and the crackling of the fires in the villages.

People fled in panic and a general chaos resulted. The occupation of Moscow seemed imminent. And then, again, as it had done more than a century before, a powerful ally joined the demoralized Soviet forces. The weather god succeeded in what the Russians failed to do despite their display of power, despite the sacrifice of millions of citizens. It rained and snowed uninterruptedly. The earth sucked up the dampness like a sponge, and the German attack got stuck in the knee-deep mud.

Almost four weeks of rain made all roads impassable for tactical movements, as well as for supply. The defenders had time to collect their strength. New troops were brought in from Siberia and three strong defense lines were established in front of Moscow. And the people of Moscow felt relieved.

The danger, only eighty kilometers from the Kremlin, had vanished for the moment.

"Der Alte wird uns helfen! The Old Man will help us!" was frequently whispered by the invaders. Their legendary Barbarossa, the "sleeper-hero," was expected to aid his troubled people. Yet, still, the vehicles of the invincible Nazi forces were stuck in the Russian mud. On the Smolensk-Moscow ridges and in the swamps of the Moskva Valley they lolled helplessly. Every step became exertion. The more work performed, the deeper the vehicles and the heavy guns sank. Snowchains, tow chains, winches, engineers, construction teams, and drivers were applied to the problems. But nothing moved through the brownish-gray bottomless brew.

In addition, the Russians added to the desperation of the invading forces by introducing an unexpected weapon, the T-34 tank. The tanks were placed in special underground garages from which they were able to emerge quickly and into which they disappeared after having fired several volleys into the enemy. The defenders also staggered the aggressor with their modern motorized rocket launchers which discharged sixteen projectiles at a time.

Boost's Supply Company, as a part of the eastward movement, dragged themselves silently through the mud. Their feet were soaking wet and their legs froze. Clay-smeared overcoats hung heavily under the wet shelter halves. Only the glowing cigarette butts in the corners of the mouths were dry and warm.

The road was too narrow to form a proper march column, and the infantry trod along in long rows on both sides of the muddy deluge. No proud goose step. No songs. During the occasional rest periods, the soldiers consumed their food rations hastily in the road ditch. At night they lay somewhere, man on man, to enjoy a little warmth before standing guard.

No one rode. The horses had to be spared. For a long time, there had been no oats. Hay was occasionally found, but most villages were left in heaps of ashes by the retreating peasants.

Approaching the front lines, the infantry was repeatedly engaged in heavy fighting with the fresh Siberian troops and numerous Soviet armored brigades.

"For a defeated people the Russians are fighting quite well!" Boost's second in command remarked. After all, the Führer himself had proclaimed Nazi victory on the eastern front some time ago. No one could comprehend why the Russians continued so obstinately.

"Obviously they understood nothing the Führer had said. They should have been taught our Muttersprache prior to the Führer's proclamations and they might have complied," Boost remarked half jokingly.

As it was, the stubborn "Rusky," as the invaders called their enemy, persisted in the defense of his "holy city." It puzzled the aggressor that the people continued such a seemingly hopeless struggle. The Führer had promised his armies a quick victory. Victories over the western front had proved the Nazis were invincible. They knew it. The Führer boasted it and the whole Reich believed it.

"But do the Russians know it?" Boost allowed himself to think out loud. The soldiers jested about their ironic fate secretly at first, but the jokes became bolder with the realization that the few spies among them were too busy drying their own socks to be overly concerned with "innocent" remarks of the troops.

"Our troops are advancing on Moscow! It is only a matter of days, and they will parade before our glorious Führer on the Red Square!" Seemann exclaimed excitedly before the assembled work camp.

From the first day of the "Barbarossa" invasion against the Soviet Union, the Mamzehr kept us informed about its progress. With each triumphant report, our hopes dipped a degree lower. The shadows grew numberless above our shtetl, and many desperate men and women joined them in a suicide epidemic, the only act of defiance they dared to commit. And while the depleted ranks of workers were replenished daily by newcomers, our hatred for the enemy grew proportionate to his successes.

"We must hold out, little brother," Roman kept saying, "we must hold out till the day comes when we shall see our enemy in the garb of a prisoner! It must happen, Wilek. It must come for Mother and Felusia. We must survive or no one will be there to say Kaddish."

"But how?"

"We must hate!" The word had majesty.

Seemann's reports continued for six agonizing weeks. Each morning we listened to the Mamzehr's ecstatic outpourings and each day we learned to hate a little more.

Finally the day came when Herr Seemann was silent.

"Can you hear them? Can you hear the big guns?" Roman would wake me in the night and we would both listen intently to the distant rumbling of the great artillery.

"I can hear them well enough, but whose are they? How do we know whose they are?"

"They are *ours*, I tell you. They must be ours!" It was a strange-sounding word, *ours*. Yet, it was an inspiring word, and as I went back to sleep, I dismissed the doubts which might have led me to believe that it was not artillery at all, but the distant thunder of an autumn storm.

On the 23rd of October the spearhead of the Tenth Panzer Division had reached the crossroads between Shchelkovka and Dorochovo, twenty-one kilometers east of Mozhaysk, on the large highway from Smolensk to Moscow.

The highway was the only passable, traffic-bearing road to the main artery of operations of the central front. The Soviets realized that too well and the first forces they could muster were employed against that crossroad.

On the 25th of October the Seventh German Infantry Division, coming from Vereya, relieved the Tenth Panzer Division in the area around Shchelkovka. Heavy Soviet artillery fired into this relief instantly. On the following day, the Führer's Seventh Infantry Division tried to advance from the crossroads eastward in order to break the Soviet onslaught on that important central traffic point. Simultaneously, the Soviets were ordered to seize the crossroads and break through toward Mozhaysk. Attack upon attack broke loose. The riflemen encountered a completely fresh Bolshevik Far Eastern Division—the 82nd Soviet Rifle Division from Outer Mongolia, reinforced by two armored brigades, subordinate rifle regiments, artillery, and rocket launchers. The earth quivered under the force of their intense firepower and the German riflemen dug their resistance pockets in the mud. Tank after tank of the Soviets rolled on. All of Shchelkovka became one big witches' cauldron. The peasant shacks flared as they burned to the ground. Into this inferno jumped the soil colored figures of the Mongolians as they gradually advanced.

Several companies of the 19th Infantry Regiment fired their few remaining rounds before retreating to the north-south road, Rusa-Vereya. Replenishing their ammunition, they dug in again. Engineers came to their aid with concentrated charges and mines and the antitank teams, with their armor-piercing missiles, halted the approach of the Russian "iron bunkers" as they moved through the ruins of Dorochovo, along the railroad, and through the wooded area which encircled that locality. That thin front of the German infantry division managed to last through all the critical hours even though the Soviets brought on fresh replacements continuously. Finally, on the 27th of October, the mighty, continuous attack was ended. Only the Soviet artillery was still firing its heavy, screaming shells. Both Shchelkovka and Dorochovo were debris, but they were still firmly in the invader's hands, as was the crossroad.

The Russians suffered. According to an intercepted radio message, 45 per cent of their newly manufactured tanks had already dropped out. Almost fourteen hundred Soviet soldiers were captured.

The invader also had many painful casualties. The grave-mounds with steel helmets increased on the crossroad and, although the Russians could not take the crossroad itself, they controlled the streets nearby. Orderly supply traffic was impossible. Only a few daring drivers succeeded in getting through.

The invading forces commenced an attack to remove the steady Russian danger to the crossroads and to open it again for traffic. By daybreak all three divisions of the Seventh Army Corps with the support of the 11th detachment of the 31st Panzer Regiment of the Fifth Panzer Division moved out to push the defenders back to the east. Attack after attack was tossed back because the Soviets had once again designated the same day for a renewed assault. A captured order of the 82nd Soviet Motorized Rifle Division showed clearly the intentions of the defenders. The first two numbers of the order read:

1. PARTS OF THE GERMAN 19TH INFANTRY REGIMENT RENDER STUBBORN RESISTANCE IN DOROCHOVO. THEIR MORTARS AND SINGLE SMALL CALIBER GUNS FIRE OUT OF BASEMENTS AND THE M.G.'S FROM THE ROOFS OF HOUSES.

2. THE COMMANDER OF THE 210TH MOTORIZED RIFLE REGIMENT IS TO PREPARE AN ATTACK ON DOROCHOVO DURING THE NIGHT FROM THE 1ST TO THE 2ND OF NOVEMBER, 1941, AND THE RAILROAD STATION IN DOROCHOVO AS WELL AS THE CROSSROAD WEST OF DOROCHOVO IS TO BE TAKEN.

The order was signed by the commanding officer, the regimental commissar, and the chief of staff of the 82nd Motorized Rifle Division. After heavy artillery barrages by both sides, the German and Soviet assault troops met at daybreak. Pitiful, casualty-ridden fighting resulted. The armored vehicles of the Fifth Panzer Division supported the riflemen, and the initiative to act lay with the Division of the Seventh Artillery Corps. The Russians limited themselves only to the defense. Their terrain was being taken sector by sector by the invader. The tanks pushed forward, destroying heavy infantry weapons within the Soviet lines. Then they waited and gave supporting fire to the infantry company fighting its way forward on both sides of the streets. The assault gradually gained ground, although the German tanks had to move between many mines and fight heavy antitank defenses. Strong counterattacks by the Soviet tank units were fought off. Shortly before the first German armored cars arrived at a river sector, the bridges had been smashed into the mud. Crossings had to be found through the undergrowth and the swamp, all between mines and all under Soviet fire.

The Russians defended their soil stubbornly until the last moment. They kept trying to set the German armored cars on fire with their Molotov cocktails. There were considerable losses, especially among the infantry. Even the combat cars (Panzerwagen) which were confined to the roads due to the muddy terrain met with considerable losses. Further attack was halted on the evening of the 4th of November.

It was not an autumn storm after all. The big guns thundered uninterruptedly day and night, and since there were no customary Appell announcements, we surmised that all was not proceeding for the enemy as planned.

164

Ironically, the enemy's reverses also became our own. The turnip soup was thinner than usual, and we spent our time vainly attempting to fish a morsel of horse meat out of the daily ration. The enemy introduced various types of Ersatz such as margarine extracted from coal and bread that tasted more like sawdust each day. Even the occasional handouts from our few Polish friends began to dwindle; a baked potato was truly thought of as a meal "fit for a king."

In addition, it had become increasingly difficult to obtain medication from the dispensary. Following Forster's decline, Dr. Franz Gomberg was placed in charge, and he swiftly proceeded to establish a completely new set of regulations for use of the dispensary. Once installed in the position he had coveted all along, Gomberg was a man to be trusted. He was unmercifully thorough and relentlessly vindictive. He promptly discharged his former chief Jablonski, who was assigned to the factory with the rest of us. The young physician's health declined, but he dared not go to his former associate for aid. His beautiful wife Masha was transferred to the "special" women's quarters to provide pleasure for the gods.

"Tomorrow I must take a day from work, I'll fake something, maybe a stomach-ache, or something, but I must rest up a bit." Roman was becoming weaker each day. With the heat from the great furnace sapping every inch of liquid from our bodies and the lack of nourishment, we were all near exhaustion.

"You can't! You know what Gomberg will do, he'll report you to the Mamzehr, it's not like it used to be anymore," I pleaded.

"I'll drop in my tracks, Wilek, I must have some food, or I'll drop!"

"Think of what you told me. Think of their defeat. It's coming, Roman, it's nearer each hour. We must go on, we'll do something."

That night I raided the refuse cans behind the factory

kitchen. A pocketful of egg shells and potato peels. We consumed them secretly and greedily in our bunks before going to sleep. After a while, our teeth had gotten accustomed to the dissonant sound of grinding lime and our stomachs reconciled themselves to digesting refuse. We lived only for the ecstasy of revenge.

On November 4th came the first significant cold wave with occasional snow falling. The thermometer dropped below freezing and continued to fall. Soon the vast Russian expanse was covered with snow. The bitter cold froze both man and war machine. Only the deepest swamps remained partially viscous, adding to the despair of the invader whenever a crossing was attempted.

The Tenth Panzer Division, which had been released at the crossroad of Shchelkovka by the Division of the Seventh Army Corps, advanced to the north across the Moskva through the small town of Rusa toward Novo-Petrovskoye, to endanger Moscow from the northwest. The advance was to go on till the last fuel was consumed, the last bread eaten, and the last shells fired. According to the laws of the Blitzkrieg, one had to pursue a defeated enemy "to the last breath of man and horse." But the Germans could move further only with the greatest of efforts. The railroad had to carry fuel, ammunition, and supplies through gigantic detours because blown-up bridges had closed the straight route from Vyazma. Everywhere between Smolensk and Vyazma the invaders feverishly built bridges and sections of the railroads and highways. They were constantly hampered by the increased partisan activity behind their lines.

The seventy kilometer stretch of road between Gzhatsk and Mozhaysk was mud-filled with craters from the constant

Soviet shelling. Thousands of heavy trucks had to wait for better conditions in order to move on. The intersection at Shchelkovka was closed for days. Although the supply and engineering units spent every short wintery daylight hour repairing the roads, the heavily loaded supply columns were hopelessly rooted in sleet and mud. The German front line units suffered their first lack of provisions in the course of a campaign. Potatoes were served three times daily. Many a commander and general ate millet day after day while the fully loaded supply columns were unable to move forward or backward. Air supply was also out of the question because the airfields resembled the roads.

Overnight deeper frost and blizzards set in, and the invaders' last fuel reserves had to be used to keep the motors of their tanks running. The armored personnel lived in ditches dug beneath their tanks and although relatively safe from Soviet artillery shells, the foxholes provided little or no shelter from the cold.

Had not Boost's feet been previously dried, they would have hung from his body like two ice blocks. He and his companions dug in underground and in caves at the forest edges. Only a small blue smoke spiral between the pine tops, betrayed the nest of twelve to fifteen men, tightly pressed together around an improvised tin stove, freezing in semidarkness. They thought of the fresh supplies of ammunition, fuel, rations, and winter clothing which they carried for distribution, but did not dare guess when the roads would become passable again.

It had become increasingly more difficult to deliver supplies. The ranks of the Verpflegungskompanie were decimated in their untiring effort to bring food to their comrades. The foxholes were difficult to spot because of the incessantly falling snow. However, the moving supply men were easily picked off by the Siberian marksmen.

"Every German you pick off will break the morale of at

least ten others," Sgt. Ivan Schepiloff said to his Siberian sniper unit assigned to the task of disrupting the invader's communications. His men were well trained and well equipped. They wore white snowsuits, impregnable fur boots, and spread destruction with high-powered rifles.

Boost was desperate. He was losing his best men and there was no evidence that the lines had received their supplies. All he had left was a detachment of replacements, boys in their late teens at most. And he understood that this was no war for children. The people of a besieged land had risen to defend their mother earth and theirs was the strength of a people pushed to the utmost.

Swinging a large sack of provisions over his shoulder, Boost shouted some last-minute orders to his youthful second in command, Schroeder, and ran. For some time his men could follow the dark spot moving swiftly from one foxhole to another. There was actually hope he might succeed. From behind a fir tree Schepiloff slowly raised his rifle to his shoulder. "We both do our duty," he repeated stubbornly as he squeezed the trigger. The shot resounded and echoed through the vast white fields. Boost took a few more steps and stumbled slowly through the snow. He would soon be frozen into the landscape.

In spite of the supply problems, German units were feverishly active and finally the corduroy road—45,000 logs put together side by side—was completed. But the frost also gave partial maneuverability to the Soviets and they attacked incessantly to cut off the main traffic artery and the advancing Panzer division which pointed toward the east like a thorn. Nazi telephone cables were cut and connections could not be made. The wounded, many with second and third degree frostbite, were moved only with great difficulty back from the front line. The corduroy was cleaned with considerable effort and security measures were taken to the rear of the long road.

Schroeder was one of the many who stood, weapons ready to fire, guarding the precious corduroy road. Around them there was nothing except loneliness and cold. The visibility was less than ten meters and except for the sporadic firing, everything was quiet. Schroeder thought about Boost. He froze and trampled his feet warm. Occasionally a branch broke. He listened. The dark forest was silent and Schroeder had the feeling he was being watched by a thousand eyes. Should he have given the alarm? One signal would have called the relief men who sat in the earth hole warming themselves around a small fire. But an experienced soldier gives the alarm only when there is a definite cause. Two hours of guard passed in constant tension. He looked forward to warming up a little by the fire and dozing off in a light slumber until his turn came up again.

The division headquarters was located at the middle of the advance column in Pokrovskoye. Russian artillery destroyed the poorly constructed quarters, blowing up the cottages one after another. Numerous casualties depleted the staff. Although the Germans knew their situation was difficult, the general—with the Ritterkreuz on his sweater—was calm and confident. Now and then the guards succeeded in capturing one of the Soviet spies; they were mostly villagers and included women and children. When the bombardment finally became too intolerable, the invaders withdrew to a neighboring village, leaving Schroeder's small detachment to occupy the area.

The "occupying" force moved into the only sturdy building left, the large white stone church. There they lay at the foot of the vaults on meager spreads of hay. A large cylindrical iron stove filled the room with heat and stinging smoke. The only two pieces of furniture, a shaky table and chair, were confiscated by the company commander. Now and then the earth shook, but most of the fighting was going on at Skirminovo and Marino.

At Skirminovo and Marino the Soviets launched repeated attacks. From the nature of the wounded, one could see the toughness of the 78th Siberian Rifle Division. Those who could still move crawled through the snow on their stomachs to the glowing ashes of the burned houses to protect themselves from the cold. Men who had been exposed to the bare ice of swamps for many nights were found alive and alert.

The Siberians attacked with the support of the Elite Tank Brigade. The heavy armored cars were whitewashed and could not be recognized in the fog. Nevertheless, the Germans were still intercepting the overwhelming advance of Soviet troops.

The field phone rang. Sgt. Schepiloff reached out with a sudden jerk. Although he only uttered a few formal military expressions, his face was animated and beaming with excitement. He replaced the receiver with a final "Khorosho" and ordered his small sniper unit to withdraw. They were to rejoin their unit. Things were in progress which no one could surmise. They dared not talk, but the air was tense with the anticipated move.

Each time Soviet armor appeared on the scene there was desperate fighting. The Germans had to dig many graves. Their numb and frozen hands worked strenuously for hours digging in the stone-like earth. They laid hardfrozen clay chunks on their commanders and officers as a last farewell. But they did not give up the battle. Broadcasts, although infrequent, shouted news of great German successes to the north and south of the eastern front. "Soon we shall start up again in front of Moscow!" and slowly one Nazi supply truck after another made it to the head of the armored columns. Slowly the invaders chopped themselves out of the frozen mud in the rear. Then the news came of an SS division advancing through Rusa accompanied by a fresh unit of the infantry. They were the divisions of the Ninth Army Corps under the command of General of the Infantry Geyer. The enemy prepared for another all-out attack on Moscow.

The Soviets, however, did not sit by idly. They knew the German troop movements and through constant harassment and small skirmishes did all they could to postpone the offensive. The defenders brought pressure not only on the Fourth Panzergruppe but also on their left flank, the Third Panzergruppe, both of whom had assembled for a renewed attack in the area of Kalinin. The right flank of the Fourth Panzergruppe Hoepner, the Fourth Army Corps, also felt the renewed diversionary movements of the Soviets fighting to gain time.

Meanwhile, the high German command planned the new all-out offensive on Moscow before the arrival of heavy snow and more cold. Time was getting shorter. Decisions were made. The crack SS Fourth Panzergruppe was ordered to break through the newly formed defense lines. They were to outflank and cut off Moscow from the north and northeast.

The first one-and-a-half weeks of that short early winter period were used to bring up further supplies and troops. Small local penetrations were made to establish bridgeheads, to straighten the front line, and to take prisoners for interrogation in order to establish the strength and composition of the Soviet forces. When weather permitted, the army reconnaissance planes flew their missions. The generals themselves made area studies of the frontmost secured positions in order to have a personal view of the attack area.

The Soviets counted on one massive offensive push of the German forces. Tens of thousands of workers, even women and children, hastily built defenses. In nightly air raids the Soviets attempted to destroy the new German positions in front of Moscow. They hit the German supply organization and the very essential maintenance repair shop companies for tanks and armored vehicles.

In addition to the sniper activity, the Soviets unleashed a steady radio and leaflet propaganda campaign to undermine the fighting morale of their enemy. And, by the time the invader was ready to move, the Soviet defense lines stretched out before the capital. A deeply linked fortress system was located in front of the attacking German divisions. The second great Moscow protective position stretched from Klin in the north of Moscow to the Istra region. It followed the upper course of the Istra River. Immediately before Kubinskoye, it led almost directly southward across Naro-Fominsk behind the Nara along the front of Serpukhov toward Tula. The sector from Klin, directly south of the highway about one hundred kilometers wide, stretched in front of the Fourth Panzergruppe. Besides this road and the Volokolamsk-Moscow highway, there were no other solid traffic roads. The Soviet capital lay directly ahead of the front. The defenders, therefore, had complete control over all advantages of the "inner line." The Soviet air force had the use of the hangars and repair shops of the Moscow airfields, while the German planes often had to stand on the snowed-in provisional airfields, where they were continually subject to strafing and severe weather conditions.

According to all calculations, the Russians were able to look forward to the new German attack against Moscow with a certain degree of confidence. They had been able to mass at least ten Rifle Divisions, four of which were Siberian, in front of the Panzergruppe to form the primary line of resistance. There were also an additional seven armored brigades with five hundred to six hundred new tanks. These brigades were moveable reserves behind the front and could, if necessary, push the advanced Germans out of the protective line by counterattacks. Numerous artillery pieces and rocket launcher regiments were added to those formations. On the 16th of November the Fourth Panzergruppe of the Fifth

Corps opened its attack from the north in the direction of Moscow.

Intelligence maps revealed to the Germans a second great protective line of Moscow, Klin, Istra, Svenigorod, Naro-Fominsk, Sepurkhow, and Tula, behind which the Soviet capital sat like a spider in the web of its numerous traffic connections. The German armed forces were well over a thousand kilometers from their supply bases during their siege of Moscow, and the traffic roads from the Reich to the Moscow front were totally deficient.

Under the command of General of the Infantry Ruoff, the Fifth Corps renewed its attack on the 16th of November. Combined with the Second Panzer Division and the 35th and 196th Infantry Divisions from the area of Volokolamsk, the offensive pushed toward the east against Klin. They were to meet with the First Corps on the left flank of the Fourth Panzergruppe. The 23rd Infantry Division followed as reserve. The First Corps had the mission of taking the city of Klin in order to turn to the southeast and cut off Moscow from the north. This maneuver led to heavy fighting with the defenders trying to prevent the dangerous encirclement of their capital.

Most unexpectedly, the Mamzehr appeared before the assembled inmates on a cold November morning, wearing ear-muffs and heavy woolen gloves, his boots impeccably shiny. He breathed heavily into the cold air, the steam emphasizing the bitter cold. He was visibly excited.

"Well, we're in for it, the Mamzehr has news he wants to share with us."

"This can mean only one thing: they're winning again."

"Silence!" The order came from one of the guards. The chief god ascended the makeshift platform.

"He looks altogether too happy, I'm worried," Roman whispered.

"We'll have ample time to worry later; let's hear what he has to say." I preferred to worry with a reason. We had often wondered about the Mamzehr's profession in private life. His stage presence was excellent. He knew how to keep his audience in suspense and at a high pitch of excitement.

"You have probably wondered why I have discontinued my daily reports to you! It was because there were things in the making which were none of your business!" He looked around to examine the effect of his words.

"Great things have happened since we last chatted together." He used the familiar *euch.*

"Here it comes now; the Mamzehr wants something and he is hedging around it," Shlomo whispered behind us.

"The combined armed forces of the Reich have launched a massive attack on all points of the eastern front! We have received news of numerous victories despite the severe cold and heavy defenses. The Soviet soldiers desert their ranks in great numbers to join the liberating armies."

"Lies, lies, nothing but lies," Shlomo seethed, "He received his news directly from Herr Goebbels, the boldest liar of them all."

"The war effort must double from this day on! We have received orders from the Reichsführer himself to increase production immediately!" the Mamzehr continued unperturbed.

"There's the catch! You see? What did I say?" Roman could not contain himself. "Now we'll never make it!"

"In the days ahead, you will witness history as it never occurred before!"

"The Mamzehr missed the sixth grade entirely," Shlomo remarked, "now he teaches his own history lesson."

The Mamzehr's own interpretation of history was indeed hard to digest. Production was raised to new heights under the jealous vigilance of our zealous gods. We were assigned work details arbitrarily, consisting for the most part of unloading incoming freight trains of raw materials or loading the finished product onto the departing transports. We worked an average of eighteen hours a day. We were accomplices of the enemy.

On November 17 the fog lifted at 0900 hours after a misty morning and permitted a clear view of the frosty winter scenery. A group of SS officers stood on a ridge just east of Mussino at the observation point of a battery. The edge of a wood ran along a distance of three thousand meters, vanishing into the horizon. Plain fields, kilometers in width, stretched between the ridges and the forest, with a few dark brown bushes here and there. Grain stubble and some sharp furrows shone through the light snow ceiling. The sun gradually climbed higher. One of the German regiments was to push toward the north and situate itself behind the main line ready for the attack. It was then 1000 hours.

Young Schroeder, promoted to Unteroffizier in charge of his own supply unit, was part of the SS detachment at Mussino. He had joined the SS officers at the observation point and felt proud and important. Eager to impress his fierce companions, the youthful noncom was especially watchful.

In the direction of attack Schroeder suddenly perceived sixty to seventy horsemen, who disappeared into the woods after a few artillery shots were fired at them. Since they had been expected, no special significance was attributed to their sudden movement north. The village of Porfinikovo was on the right of the observing officers. It had already been the showplace of heavy infantry battles and was once again under Soviet fire.

Suddenly four tanks appeared. They drove directly at their target. Only once did they stop short to form a small circle. The observers on the ridge asked themselves why their concealed tank howitzers and antitank guns on the edge of the village held their fire.

Indeed, no infantry followed the rolling and continually firing steel giants, but penetration seemed imminent. However, behind the guns and cannons stood battle-proven SS who had destroyed several tanks at point blank range. Their steel ruins served as weird reminders. Suddenly, the lead tank exploded into black smoke. Then the three remaining ones were hit. Slowly they burned out. None of the crew was seen leaving the flaming structures.

While all attention was still directed at the quick skirmish, a sudden command was heard. The division commander spotted a considerably large number of horsemen, who soon disappeared behind frost-covered trees. Orders were telephoned. Salvos exploded. Soon the Siberian riders reappeared three thousand meters in front of the village line. First there were a few, then fifty, one hundred, three hundred men. New masses broke from right and left, from east to west. The Germans stood bewildered. They could not believe that the Soviets would attack on a widely open parade ground.

Nevertheless, with unbelievable speed, the horsemen formed skirmish lines one after another and then a third rank from the rear. The last file set far off from the woods, broke off to the left, and galloped southward.

It was an indescribably beautiful picture, the bright winter landscape and a cavalry regiment in a full charge; stirrup on stirrup, the horsemen bent deep in the saddle wielding glittering sabers.

Schroeder kept rubbing his eyes in disbelief. The Mongol

storms seemed to have returned. The small, black, shaggy horses with the saddle-grown Asiatics impetuously streamed into the Occident. "The poor devils," he murmured to himself. "At least then they had an even chance. Those were the days!" His contemplation was suddenly interrupted by the voice of a young officer nearby.

"The fools are begging for it! Smash them to bits!"

The batteries fired from open firing positions. The projectiles blended with the red fire-trailing shells of antitank weapons. From the village south of the advance SS position all barrels were blasting. A single cloud barrier of exploding shells hovered over the oncoming cavalry squadrons. The charge did not falter. In that mass of fire an inexplicable right turn was completed, and the spearhead of the regiment stormed into the open side of the horseshoe-shaped village.

At the head of the advancing horsemen was Sergeant Schepiloff. His squad was headed straight at the embankment position under Unteroffizier Schroeder's command. The horsemen were no further than fifty yards from the embankment when the terrified Schroeder shouted "Feuer!"

This was no mirage of the past. The small black creatures stained the snow. Animal guts spilled on dying riders.

"Mein Gott," Schroeder exclaimed, "they've gone stark mad." His right forefinger squeezed the trigger of his air-cooled machine gun. There was a strange fascination and his finger kept on pressing the hot metal more fiercely than he wished it to. He felt an ineffable joy.

The rapid rifle fire of Schroeder's men unseated many, but the momentum of the attack carried the remainder into their midst. "Death to the dogs!" Schepiloff's saber cut the startled invader's neck from one shoulder to the other. There was no time for the German to shout with pain. Only the eyes carried the mark of terror as the head rolled into the snow. Moments later Schepiloff was caught by an enemy bullet. His shaggy little horse ran on a while longer, without direction.

The German artillery was organized into an effective ricochet fire. Horses flew through the air and fell to the ground torn to shreds. Horsemen whirled one on another. The leadership was lost. The animals, wild in the exploding hell, galloped in all directions, crowding together in their terror, trampling everything living under their hoofs. The few riders who managed to stay in the saddle disappeared in the concentrated mass. Artillery hit repeatedly into the havoc, and with the added devastation of antitank shells, the last vestige of an attack crumbled to bits.

Into this terror a second cavalry regiment charged bravely from the same point of the forest. It was weird and incredible that the same spectacle would be repeated after the bloody defeat of an entire regiment. The distance and the direction of the attack was well known from the previous encounter and full annihilation proceeded even faster. Thirty riders, led by an officer with a high-raised saber on a beautiful fast horse, almost reached the village as the only survivors of the nearly thousand men. They fell attempting a valiant leap over the gun emplacements.

The white, snow-covered plains, empty and calm half an hour ago, were a red-spotted winding sheet on which numerous dark dots lay moving jerkingly; others lay still, very still. The exhausted little Cossack horses came toward the edge of the wood into the village and near the machine gun ridge. The high saddles were empty. One could see here and there a few cavalry men crawl strenuously to cover, and a few in shock wandered about the area. That which thirty minutes earlier had come roaring up in a thunderous charge lay shattered in the hail of shells.

A deep stillness came over the battlefield. Silently the SS observed the destruction. As if compelled by a secret impulse, they raised their hands in a final salute to a valiant opponent. Then came the sound of sharp orders, and the regiment began to attack.

The Fifth Corps moved forward. The adjacent unit of the Third Panzergruppe joined the advance along the Volga sector and the first targets were reached. As early as November 23 the 106th Infantry Division was at Klin; the Second Panzer Division had already taken Ssolnetschnogorsk. The big highway and the Moscow-Leningrad Railroad were also in German hands. On November 24 the 35th Infantry Division encircled the Istra sector from the north and took the village of Novinki. And while the Fifth Corps turned south toward Moscow, the divisions of the Third Panzergruppe from Klin began further to envelop the Soviet capital.

Heavy fighting developed. The SS Division Reich was confronted with the 78th Siberian Rifle Division, which held on desperately to every village, forest, and stream sector and because of its valor was called the Ninth Garde Division. Bloody close combat fighting was common. The SS had a special score to settle with the Siberians. Soviets were slain by the hundreds in the burning village, but white birch death runes placed on the SS graves revealed equal losses in the invader's ranks.

On the 25th of November the Second Panzer Division engaged the Soviet forces at Peschki. The Soviets were equipped with British Mark III tanks. For the first time the much-publicized English weapon made direct contact with the German soldiers in front of the besieged capital. It seemed, however, that the English tanks were even less effective than their Soviet counterparts. The Soviet crews grumbled about "the old tin cans that were turned over to Stalin as a commodity of no value."

Increasing numbers of Soviet soldiers were smoked out by the SS flamethrowers. A little later they stood huddled together in their wide, billowing coats, fur caps, and felt boots in the midst of glittering bayonets. The surrendered weapons were pushed into the snow by SS men. Then the prisoners were marched to the rear.

On the eve of the 26th of November, the Istra sector, the second Soviet defense line before Moscow, fell. That same night heavy Soviet artillery, rockets, and infantry counterattacked up to forty meters from the German security lines. On the 27th of November, after establishing bridgeheads south of the Klaisma, the spearheads of the Fifth Corps were directly north of the Klaisma Dam. By the 1st of December their left flank managed to reach the Moskva-Volga canal near Dmitrov and Yachova. From the furthermost security outposts of the Fifth Corps it was only twenty-three kilometers to the Kremlin. In nineteen days the invaders had advanced 120 kilometers from their starting point. Three panzer divisions, the SS Division Reich, and the Panzergruppe Hoepner, were within walking distance of the Kremlin.

But the weather gods came to the aid of the "holy city." The temperature dropped to thirty-four degrees below zero and the winds were ice whips. A "Special" order came directly from the Commanding General of the Ninth Corps. A copy was dispatched to the Führer himself.

CORPS ORDER OF THE DAY!

THE 5TH OF DECEMBER 1941

THE DIVISION AND ARMY TROOPS OF THE IX CORPS HAVE DESTROYED THE OPPOSING TENACIOUS ENEMY IN THREE SHARP EVENLY LED BLOWS FROM NOVEMBER 19TH TO 22ND, HAVE PUSHED THROUGH AND DESTROYED HIS FRONT LINE OF ABOUT 25 KM IN WIDTH, AND FINALLY TO A DEPTH OF ALMOST 50 KM.

THE SUCCESSFUL ADVANCE HAD TO BE STOPPED, BECAUSE IT WAS POSSIBLE FOR THE ENEMY TO BRING UP FRESH FORCES. MOST OF ALL, HOWEVER, THE CHANGE OF WEATHER BROUGHT WITH IT WIND AND EXTREME COLD WHICH REDUCED THE PROSPECT OF FULL MECHANIZED UTILIZATION IN THE FUTURE ASSAULTS TO SUCH AN EXTENT THAT THE

RESOLUTION FOR THE TEMPORARY SURRENDER OF THE
ADVANCE AND PARTIAL REGRESSION FROM THE FRONT HAD
TO BE MADE.

LEADERSHIP AND TROOPS' ACCOMPLISHMENTS IN THE
ATTACK WERE EXEMPLARY. THEIR ACTIONS WERE OVER
AND ABOVE THEIR CALL OF DUTY: THE HARDSHIPS OF CON-
STANT COMBAT WERE ENDURED WITH GREAT PERSONAL
STRENGTH AGAINST A CONTINUALLY HARASSING ENEMY
AS WELL AS THE OPPOSING WEATHER CONDITIONS.

I EXPRESS MY ACKNOWLEDGEMENT AND ADMIRATION
TO THE LEADERSHIP AND TROOPS. THEY HAVE PROVEN AS A
WHOLE IN INNUMERABLE SINGLE CASES THEIR AGGRESSIVE-
NESS TO THE UTMOST, THEIR HARD WILL AND BELIEF,
THEIR GREAT FIGHTING SPIRIT, AND THEIR SUPERIORITY.

WE NOW STAND IN A CLOSED FRONT. IT WILL BE
COMPLETED FOR A PERMANENT POSITION, AND OUR ENEMY
WILL BE STOPPED.

HEIL MEIN FÜHRER!
YOUR COMMANDING GENERAL

Inconspicuous as it seemed, the Corps order of the day
had marked a new turn in the battle for the Soviet capital. As
a result of the ever-increasing partisan activity behind the
lines, the attack of the Fourth and Third Panzergruppen had
to be halted and defensive action taken. The offensive of the
two Panzergruppen northwest of Moscow had drawn all
available Soviet forces from the west front to Moscow. The
Russians added to these new forces all the seemingly inex-
haustible reserves of manpower of their giant land.

With the arrival of Christmas, the Führer once again
broadcast his message to the troops.

"Nächste Weihnachten sind wir zu Hause! We will be
home, come next Christmas!"

"Sieg heil!"

And it came to pass . . .

Barbarossa vanquished, and they knew not
Where his bones were laid to rest.
Was it in rivers of exotic lands, or
The frozen plains of a vast expanse?

And the sages rejoiced . . .

For the fearful Barbarossa perished
Like all tyrants from abysmal Hel.
And Odin was in his glory, to the
Despair of Loki who was drunk with hate . . .

And it came to pass . . .

The slain all came before the Æsir,
And silence befell the battlefield,
And the gods took after their judgment seats,
Determined to end all strife henceforth . . .

And it came to pass . . .

Weep ye not for the dead,
Neither bemoan him;
But weep sore for him that
*   goeth away,*
For he shall return no more,
Nor see his native country.
JEREMIAH 22:10

December 7, 1941. Japan unleashed its attack on the United States and we learned the new developments from Seemann.

"The imperial Japanese air force struck a death blow to the entire United States sea and air power. Our Japanese allies are preparing an invasion of the American mainland."

"Poor Uncle Markus," I whispered to Roman.

"Serves them right," he responded bitterly.

"Don't say that, Roman; if Japan takes America our hopes are gone."

"Silence, you miserable swine." Seemann's voice roared above our heads. "With the imminent defeat of the United States you can no longer expect your Uncle Roosevelt to come to your aid. Soon, he will join your ranks as a worker. We will do away with the Jewish world conspiracy once and for all. We shall liberate the American Aryans from Jewish oppression. Jude verrecke! Death to the Jews! Now, all of you, shout so that your brothers in America can hear you! Shout! Death to the Jews!"

"Death to the Jews!"

The inmates responded and Mamzehr looked pleased.

"I hope they make it, I hope they take over." Roman seethed the words between his teeth. "I hate the Americans almost as much as our enemy!"

"Be quiet, someone might hear you," I pleaded with my brother, but he went on.

"They're as guilty of our plight as all of the enemy put together. At least the brownshirts don't pretend they love us. They promised to do away with us, and the silence of our alleged friends is a sign of approval. They might even accomplish it."

"Roman, please."

"What have our uncles done? *Now* they go to war! A few bombs have fallen into their own backyard! *Now* they'll fight to liberate what's left of us!"

The Mamzehr observed our consternation for a while, then he continued: "There is panic in Washington, and there is panic all over the United States. The blow dealt by our Japanese allies had a demoralizing effect on the capitalistic swine. The Wall Street Jews are committing suicide by the tens and hundreds. Soon there will be no one left for us to liquidate when we get there! Ha, ha, ha, good, eh?" He stopped briefly to note the effect of his humor. There was complete demoralization. But there was also deep, vindictive hatred, and he turned to face his aides. With a click of the heels of his immaculately polished boots, he raised his arm.

"Heil Hitler!"

"Heil Hitler!"

"Weitermachen!" He barked the order which began our working day.

Events did not, however, take the course outlined to us by the Mamzehr. The United States quickly overcame its initial shock. And, although the Japanese soon overran the Asiatic continent, the Nazis had begun to suffer serious reverses on the eastern front.

Each new report of the German defeat brought renewed hardship upon the Hortensia Camp inmates. And every bold new venture of the increasingly active resistance wrought proportionate reprisals in the camp as well as in the town of Piotrkow. Entire families were taken as hostages. All were shot after days of futile interrogations and torture.

Most of the SS men attached to the Piotrkow garrison had left for the eastern front. Our factory overseers attempted to camouflage their feverish preparations for an eventual evacuation with all their pedantry and efficient officialese, but we drew our own conclusions from the sight of the frequent couriers arriving at Seemann's office. Moreover, the contents of the dispatches were promptly delivered to us by the Mamzehr's "trusted" orderly, Menasha Abramowicz, our cousin twice removed, the grandnephew of Srulko Malpo. I remember Menasha telling Roman, "The enemy is getting ready to move us. If you want to make a break for it, now is the time. He'll be licking his Soviet wounds and his alertness will drop."

"We'll have to move before our enemy recovers," Roman admitted.

"The sooner, the better." Menasha shook his head meaningfully.

"I don't think Wilek and I will go over the fence this time," Roman said. "But I'd sure as hell want Hayim situated with some goyim before we're moved."

We had grown fond of Nora's cousin and did not wish to separate from him, but Yurek Skowron, a friend of the family, said he could hide one of us. It was a most difficult decision, for we had no way of knowing that we would actually help Hayim by making him a fugitive. Hayim, however, did not object. Silent acceptance of circumstance had become a way of life for all of us.

During the following weeks even the guards abandoned their usual secrecy, and we gathered that the big move would come within the next two weeks, on a Sunday. We had to act fast.

Coal was soon to be delivered to the camp, and we knew that we had to be among those unloading it or suffer the penalty of waiting for another opportunity for Hayim's escape. It snowed constantly for several days, which favored our plans. On Saturday morning Menasha placed our names on the coal detail. Yurek was notified and by noon we were on our way to the rail ramp at the far end of the camp. The blizzard continued.

By nightfall we all resembled miners. The black powder penetrated our clothing and skin; our lungs were filled with it and the annoying tickle caused outbursts of violent coughing. We unloaded the coal onto a pile a fair distance from the wagon. Away from the solitary light on the wagon an individual was not easily distinguished in the heavily falling snow.

"Hope Yurek is on time," I whispered to Roman.

"Don't worry, he will be," Roman replied, nervously glancing at Hayim, who kept throwing large coal pieces onto the wheelbarrow with his bare hands.

"This is the last one!" Roman said, grasping the wheelbarrow by the handles. "You know what to do when we get to the clearing, Hayim?"

The boy nodded. Roman lifted the load. He was aided on both sides by myself and Hayim. At about thirty paces from the wagon, neither the guard at the wagon nor the one at the receiving end could be seen clearly.

"Yurek waits beyond the clearing to the left! Hurry, Hayim! God be with you!" The sound of his quick steps was muffled by the blanket of snow.

"Hope we did the right thing."

"There wasn't much else we could do," Roman repeated several times.

A whole week of preparation for the evacuation had passed since Hayim's escape. Now the waiting was over. A detachment of SS arrived from Lodz and herded us into the boxcars. There were many onlookers present. Some were friendly; others shouted,

"Good riddance!"

"Get on, you filthy dogs!"

"You'll make a good cake of soap!"

We were among the first to climb into the wagon. Instinctively, we hurried toward the corner. About six feet from the floor there was a narrow window—one of the four in the boxcar—boarded from the outside with not too heavy lumber. On the floor, here and there, there were traces of cattle excrements which contributed to an unhealthy atmosphere. Finally, when the car was loaded the sliding door was sealed tightly behind us and we found it difficult to accustom our vision to the darkness and our nostrils to the stench.

"I don't know how long we can last, but we'll last longer near the window," Roman said. He pressed his hand against the window boards; they gave a little.

"They must have economized on the nails," he whispered, "we'll manage."

We heard some shouting from the distance. A few shots followed. We tried in vain to see through the cracks in the wall.

"Probably some poor devil tried to escape," Menasha said.

"Why would anyone, under the very noses of our keepers?"

"Instinct, little brother, instinct. No man likes to be cooped up like an animal," came Roman's reply.

"But, why . . . ?"

"Some feel stronger about it than others," Roman went on. "They can't wait, no matter what happens to them."

"Wonder what would happen if we all ran, all at once,"

Menasha mused. "They couldn't shoot us all. Some would get away. Maybe we'd even get some of them in the process. Maybe?"

"Yes, but who would be the ones to get shot?" I interjected.

"We would have to take our chances. Chance is all that is left for us now anyway."

"Don't get excited now, Menasha," Roman interrupted the melancholy outburst. "We still have hope. See the window? The time will come."

"If you're thinking of . . ."

"Quiet! Quiet, little brother. This is no time for discussions." He looked around. "No telling what a man would do for a slice of bread or some fresh air. Men have been betrayed for less than that."

"But we can't do anything to hurt the others."

"Think *only* of *yourself* now—*only* of yourself! No one else will do it for you."

The train started with a characteristic kling-klang of metal against metal. Soon we could hear no more insults, no more shouting—Polish or German. Only the wagon wheels repeated their peculiar melody as the train gained momentum.

"Let's eat," I interrupted the silence.

On boarding the train we had been given our daily food ration, two hundred grams of bread. We divided part of the rations and sat chewing them as long as they would last. Others must have taken the clue, for we could hear them smack their lips and move their jaws with relish.

"Hey, Roman, you remember the little blonde number from the polishing department?" Menasha felt like small talk.

"Yes, what of her?"

"Well, I met this little number some time ago on an errand to that section and she took a liking to me. Kasia, you know, Kasia, the girl with the long blonde pigtails."

"I told you, I remember." Roman was growing impatient.

"I'll miss her. I'll surely miss the night shifts we spent together. I really did enjoy her. She was a wonderful shikse."

"Watch out, the kid is listening."

"Aw, let him listen and learn. A little man-talk will do him a lot of good. Sooner or later he'll have to learn about the other sex. It's one of those things."

Roman continued to try to forestall my "corruption," but others in our immediate vicinity joined in on their favorite subject.

"That was one thing those shikses were good for! Now that we're gone, they'll probably go mad seducing the guys left in the factory. Would I like to be in their place!"

"That little blonde, Menasha," a voice continued, "I remember her very well. Why, she was everyone's sweetheart. By the time you got to her . . ."

"You filthy bastard!" Menasha sprang to his feet but was quickly subdued by several pairs of hands.

"Save your energy. You'll need it, Menasha." Roman tried to calm him down. "Maybe she was what they say, maybe she wasn't. What does it matter now?"

"It matters a great deal! It's only something to remember but I won't let them rob me of it!" Menasha cried bitterly.

Late into the night, long after the excitement had subsided, only a few insomniac wretches kept their worried vigil. The great majority slept, though regularly interrupted by the inadvertent mutual abuse of close quarters.

Were it not for Roman's pocket knife, which he managed to conceal during the preevacuation search, we might have lost count of time. But each day, he carved a new notch in the wall above our "bedding" to break the monotony of travel.

At the outset, the transport was halted once a day so we could attend to physical necessities under the strict surveillance of guards and receive our food rations. On the ninth day the interior of the car began to show signs of pollution. At first we coped with the problem by appointing sanitary crews to dispose of occasional excrement. But as Roman carved the fifteenth notch on the wall, conditions had deteriorated beyond control.

Almost half the inmates were down with diarrhea and we could not spare any portion of the daily water ration for cleansing. The sick, unable to muster sufficient strength to rise, lay saturated with their own putrid excretion.

"Something has to be done," Menasha said, "or we'll all be finished."

"We've got to talk to the 'Ober,'" Roman suggested. "He has to listen to reason, or he won't have any workers left when we get to wherever we're going."

"How do we know he wants us there alive?" someone remarked.

"Yes, how do we know?" came from all sides.

"They're going into too much time and expense for anything otherwise," someone said.

"We'll talk to him tomorrow; we can't go on like this."

"If only Uncle Markus could see us now!" Menasha mused. "He'd probably be glad he hadn't sent that affidavit we asked for. After all, they don't want a herd of stinking cattle in America!"

"I don't know, Roman, perhaps he did try to help."

"You can't believe that, little brother," Roman interrupted; "he didn't even take the time to reply to Dad's last letter. He was so worried about the gold we would scoop up on the streets of Brooklyn."

"Forget it now," I said, "there is little you can do about it."

"I can hate."

The train kept on moving with only occasional brief stops during which, we reasoned, other trains with higher priority were allowed to move ahead of ours. On one such occasion our guards exchanged amenities with the passing troops. It was nearing dusk, but through the cracks we could observe heavy military equipment on the slow-moving platforms. From the few fragments of conversations we had caught, we realized that the eastern front was moving westward.

"The enemy is on the run."

"A lot of good it does us," Menasha remarked, "we're right here with them."

"But we won't be much longer. Not much longer."

The train kept moving southwest. We suspected that some of the sick might have died by then, but the door would not open and the stench was becoming unbearable. The occasional complaining and painful moaning of the sick had long since completely subsided.

Destruction followeth upon destruction,
For the whole land is spoiled;
Suddenly are my tents spoiled,
My curtains in a moment.
How long shall I see the standard,
Shall I hear the sound of the horn?
JEREMIAH 4:20–21

On the twenty-first night of travel—by our own calcula-
tion we were near Kielce—the train suddenly halted. Although badly shaken in the resulting pile-up, many sighed
with relief.

"It's about time," was the general sentiment. "Let's get
this box cleaned up! Let's unload the dead!"

"Open up! Let us out!"

"Let us out, out there!"

"Open up!" Some were standing, banging on the sealed
door.

Suddenly a loud explosion shook the car, followed by
many smaller ones on all sides. Cars caught fire and the entire
place turned into an inferno. Wounding the air in their
macabre flight, bullets found their way to us and tore our
flesh to bloody bits.

"The Russians are here! Somebody open the door!
Tovarisch! Syuda!"

We shouted at the top of our voices—first in Polish, then
Russian (the language of liberty!). Roman pushed against the

small window above us. "You have to give! Give! Damn you!"

"Hurry up, Roman! I can't see. This smoke, hurry up!"

"We've got to get out!" Menasha shouted. "Let me try!" He hammered against the narrow boards and his fists were covered with blood in no time.

"I did it! I did it! Let's go!"

Those still able to move joined us. It took only seconds to stack some of the dead against the wall, climb over them, and place both our feet out the narrow opening. The heat was becoming more intense each moment.

Roman was the first to hit the ground. "Hurry up! Let's go!" One by one we jumped to the ground. The first deep breath of fresh air had an intoxicating effect. It was a misty moonless night, but in the flicker of the burning boxcars we were still able to see the distant movement of armed men and the dead SS lying about here and there.

"Hold it! Wait!" Roman held back suddenly, pointing at a group of men who had succeeded in breaking the lock of the boxcar nearest us. "Let's see what they're up to." We squatted on the ground inside a small ravine overlooking the rails. The door was rolled to one side by two of the men.

"All right now, everybody out!" We heard one of the men order the inmates to vacate the car. He spoke Polish (the language of trust). The first few men jumped to the ground. They stood joyfully awaiting further instructions. Many shouted thanks to their liberators. The insurgents waited for the last to vacate the wagon.

It took only a slight nod of the leader's head—we saw the glow of his cigarette move vertically—and his men opened fire. Before we were able to overcome our stupor, some thirty of our comrades lay dead near the tracks.

"How could they? What do they think they're doing?"

Menasha ground his teeth and clenched his blood-covered fists. "Have you ever seen anything like that? Our very own brothers!"

I wanted to run out of hiding and shout accusations at my countrymen. But instead I remained rooted to the spot, terrified.

Systematically, our "liberators" repeated their activity, putting those wagons aflame where they suspected survivors within. Soon there remained only a skeleton of heat-twisted iron. The insurgents then boarded the engine, after having gathered the SS weapons, and disappeared in the distance.

In silent anguish, unbelieving but still aware of the cruel reality, we lay for almost an hour in the ravine. Altogether there were seventeen survivors. What we had witnessed gave us the determination to fight in much broader terms than we had ever dreamed of. It widened the scope of our hatred to those whom we had hoped to befriend as comrades-at-arms.

"If it's a fight they want, a fight they'll get." Menasha was the first to break the solemn silence. "Let's salvage what's left and get going!"

We climbed cautiously out of our hiding. Although they had collected most of the automatic weapons from the dead SS, in their haste the A.K. did not make a thorough search for assorted sidearms and numerous grenades as well as an impressive amount of ammunition, which became the reward of the thorough search we conducted.

"Roman! Come here, quick!" I shouted at my brother, who was himself busy going through the pockets of a dead guard. He came running toward me.

"Look." I handed him a photograph I had found in the breast pocket of my "victim." It was a picture of the dead man, surrounded by his family, two sons and a lovely young woman. The boys could not have been over seven years of age; the woman beamed with pride as she regarded the SS insignia on her husband's uniform.

"Look at the reverse side," I said. There, barely visible, was an address: "Lindenallee 442, Berlin, S.W."

"Well, there's one Nazi who won't be triumphantly coming home to his Frau," Roman said. He was about to throw the photo to the ground.

"Why not send it to the woman? She'd appreciate knowing . . ."

"What in hell is the matter with you?" Roman yelled at the top of his voice, abandoning all caution. "Has any of the bastards sent a photo of Mother, or Grandmother, back to us after they had fried them?"

"But that's just it, Roman, that's just the point . . ."

He tore the picture into small fragments and spat after it as the pieces fell to the ground.

"What do you think we are? The Swiss Red Cross? Pick up your things and let's go!" He was calmer then. As he looked at me, he said quietly: "This is war, little brother, forget all else. There's no place for feelings in war. Anyway, I think I understand what you tried to do. Let's go."

I swung the SS man's belt across my left shoulder and stuffed my pockets full of grenades and ammunition. The German's Luger gave me a sense of security. Just as we were about to depart, I sat down on the ground, intending to pull off the guard's boots, when Yossele Moshkovitz, the tailor's son, approached us hurriedly.

"I've been looking for just such a pair of boots, let me have them."

At first I was reluctant to relinquish my prize, but after closer examination I realized that the boots were more Yossele's size than mine. Besides, he was barefoot and my shoes were still in relatively good condition. With the enemy's boots on his feet, Yossele felt ten feet tall.

Within the hour we were all ready to move out. Each of us had found some type of weapon, and the meekness of defeat and fear gave way to boldness. Nevertheless, I suspected that, if put to the test, the appearance of things far exceeded their implicit worth.

For six weeks we traveled nights, mainly on foot, aided by friendly peasants who risked their lives harboring fugitives in spite of the Seventh Bureau and ever-present informers. We worked our way to the province of Podole near the city of Rzeszow to find resistance units of the Polish Socialist Party we had heard were operating there. In our search for the friendly units we were driven by one desire: a chance to return to Treblinka to see with our own eyes what the Nazis had done with our families. For, although we had been assured by witnesses of mass exterminations, we still hoped there might be some survivors.

On our second night in the forest near Rzeszow we found ourselves surrounded by fifty rugged-looking, well-armed fighters. Their guns were cocked. Our own sentries walked slightly ahead of the intruders, their arms raised high above their heads.

"Everybody down! Belly up!" The order was given tersely in Polish and we quickly complied. At least they were not Germans.

"Get down and don't argue with the barrel of a sten gun trained on you!" Roman whispered.

"What a foolish way to die," I thought to myself. "Out here, without really knowing why. It's like dying someone else's death."

"Who's the leader of this miserable looking group of amateurs? Come on, speak up!" Startled, I looked up at the speaker. She could not have been over eighteen; a brunette dressed in men's clothing.

"Come on, come on, speak up!" The girl was getting impatient, but there was no reply we could give. During the few days we had been together as a unit, it had never occurred to us to elect a leader. Each of us made an occasional contribution and temporary "leadership" was taken for granted whenever someone's solution seemed the most applicable to a particular problem.

There was a brief silence and then, suddenly, out of the prostrated group of men, one trembling voice sang, "Voo ah-heen zol eekh gayn? Whither shall I go?"

Our captors seemed hesitant and we could hear fragments of their discussion.

"No, they couldn't be!"

"What else?"

"Let's make sure . . ."

"All right, on your feet everybody!"

"You there," the young woman pointed to Yossele. "Come closer! . . . Are you Jewish?"

"Yes," Yossele replied.

"Where do you come from?"

"Who are you? What do you want with us?" Yossele blurted out.

"You were right," she turned smilingly to one of her aides, "they're Jews. No one else would answer a question with a question!"

Everyone laughed. It was a laughter of relief and thanksgiving. Our "captors" relaxed their weapons, and we were invited to sit round the fire once again. We were given food and drink.

"We thought you were the A.K.," a bearded man said to me, pouring a second bowl of hot pea soup into the aluminum container which I held out to him. "If we hadn't heard the Yiddish . . ." He made an impressive motion with his index finger.

"Curious as it may seem, we had thought the same of you. We thought we were done for." I related our recent experience with the A.K. He understood.

"The A.K. had been ordered to eliminate as much of the potential opposition to their takeover of the country as possible," my bearded friend went on. "Particular emphasis was placed on the liquidation of socialist elements and Jews. Wherever possible, the A.K. allows the Gestapo to function. But, as you know, the A.K. frequently does the job itself."

"Aren't we all fighting the same enemy?" I asked.

My bearded friend shrugged his broad shoulders. "The A.K. fights two enemies, the Nazis and us. We avoid the Nazis in the daylight and the A.K. at night. By the way," he said as he was leaving, "my name is Anton."

That night I slept with more security than I had in a long time.

One of the many Soviet defense sections in the Istra region stretched out along the Molodilnaya. The defenders were quartered in large earthen emplacements which were heated by huge metal ovens. In comparison, the invaders occupied trenches which they called "ice cellars."

The German units were once part of the powerful Fifth Panzer Division. Decimated and badly in need of relief, they held onto their positions as ordered. A few days had gone by since their last engagement on the Volokolamsk-Istra road. Twenty-three Russian tanks, two of which were fifty-two ton units, had been knocked out but with heavy German casualties. The remainder of the Soviet armored brigade retreated to the surrounding villages behind the Molodilnaya. The Soviets fought bravely trying to defend Novo-Petrovskoye but it fell to the 46th Panzer Corps on November 21.

At the same time the Eleventh Panzer Division crossed the Istra Dam at Lopatova after removing some eleven hundred mines and two tons of explosives. And, the Germans were jubilant when they received the news of the successes of the Fifth Corps at Klin and Ssolnetschnogorsk.

The combat conditions reminded many of the fighting days in the first "big War" of the twentieth century. Rest and heat were denied the aggressors. The Soviets burned their villages, installed charges with ingenious time fuses in the larger buildings, soaked chimneys and stoves with liquid explosives. The aggressors were furious but helpless against these tactics. The already deep hatred of Bolshevism became even stronger. Having taken Novo-Petrovskoye, the aggressor settled down for a few days of well-earned but uneasy rest.

Sensing an opportunity, the Soviet command ordered a counteroffensive in the Istra sector. The initial reconnaissance activity was carried out by a relatively small combat team; riflemen, tanks, and supporting weapons rolled at dusk through the forest toward the bridgehead in German-held territory. Surprisingly, they could not be seen and the thick layers of snow also camouflaged motor noises. A Russian spearhead tank neared the lonely village of Stepankovo. The Soviet first lieutenant warmed himself in the hot air rising from the motor cowl. The tank commander stood in the turret, his observation post. They talked in subdued voices. Suddenly, a figure appeared from the shadow of a hut.

Trampling to warm his cold feet, the German trooper neared the tank. "Halt, wer kommt da!" His voice droned sleepily.

Silently humming, the tank turret swung around, until the muzzle of the cannon pointed directly at the first building. Radio communications from tank to tank followed. "Fire!" The overwhelming noise drowned out the sound of the officer's side arm as it felled the inquisitive sentry.

Flames roared through the wooden structures. Confused soldiers dressed in shirts and socks tumbled over one another as they ran through the snow to reach the safety of the forest. An entire division headquarters staff had been taken by surprise. The Russians unleashed everything they had; even anti-aircraft took part in the assault. Huts which had served as munition dumps exploded with devastating noise.

Only a quarter of an hour later, as suddenly as the holocaust had begun, a new silence set in. The tank commander radioed the news of the breakthrough to his superiors. The Soviets were on the move.

The onion-shaped towers of Istra could be seen far across the forest as the assault troops moved in long rows to the line of departure.

Very slowly the large Soviet tanks pushed ahead toward the enemy. Following them in long columns were the riflemen, fantastic to look at with their Arab-like snowshirts and steel helmets covered with white rags. Like a ghostly apparition, everything disappeared between the trees.

The enemy retreated in defense.

Supported by tank assaults, the Soviet riflemen dug the Germans out of the dirt bunkers. The forest magnified the battle noises in a thousand echoes. The heavy weapons roared. White and red tracer grenades flew like fiery streaks, searching for victims in the heavy black underbrush.

The advance of the Soviet assault marked their breakthrough on the right flank of the German IX Corps and weakened the invader's grip on Moscow. The soldiers of the IX Corps who had previously suffered heavy casualties during the muddy season were once again exposed to severe defeat. The Russian soldier was thoroughly familiar with the battle terrain and the climate. He knew how to search out his enemy and how to protect himself from the cold. The German supplies had sustained severe setbacks fighting their way into the forest of the Rusa. Even with the utmost bravery of commanders and soldiers alike, it was impossible to halt the Soviet onslaught. The Russians had succeeded in three large-scale attacks and the entire operation was completed with the occupation of the town Lokotnaya on the Rusa-Svenigrod road.

It was four weeks before our small band was sufficiently organized and trained in insurgence activities to function as a disciplined unit. The territory of our operations stretched along the Wieprz River in the wooded area between the towns Pulavy and Lubartov. Since we were never allowed to venture into the towns, our captain, the beautiful Pola, surprised us when she explained our forthcoming mission.

"There will be an armored SS convoy passing through Pulavy the day after tomorrow. The German encirclement of Moscow has been broken. These are reinforcements. They must not reach their destination in their present strength." Pola spoke tersely and I could not help thinking: "So much beauty to be wasted in destruction."

We were given our detailed instructions. Within the hour we were on our way in full force. Pola walked ahead, accompanied by her two lieutenants, Anton Niedola and Zbyszek Podrozny, who I surmised were more than merely her associates in war. My suspicions were confirmed the following evening when we reached a farm on the outskirts of Pulavy.

"What did I tell you?" Menasha remarked to Roman, with a meaningful head movement. It was then I noticed my friend Anton leaving the farmhouse.

"They must have pulled straws," Roman chuckled, "and it looks like Anton got the short end of things."

"Don't worry, he'll get his chance at midnight. She works them in shifts so there can be no jealousy. But I'll tell you one thing," he continued, "I'd like to try that myself."

At dawn Pola was at an observation post high up in the hay loft. Zbyszek stood nearby taking notes. Anton observed through his field glasses. The rumbling of tanks and the sound of heavy motor vehicles could be heard.

"Maybe this is more than we can handle, eh, Pola?" Anton remarked, lowering his binoculars.

"Don't be foolish," Pola replied, "the stronger they

are the more confident. They won't expect us and . . ."

"But there must be at least a whole SS Panzer regiment, and look at the foot soldiers! They're swarming into the village!" Anton argued.

"Are they expecting our company?" Pola asked.

"Well, no, not exactly."

"That's our superior strength! Get things ready as planned!"

The three leaders left the barn. They had a whole day to plan the operation. We did not waste our time either. Munitions were rationed out. Weapons had to be cleaned and oiled. I remembered Anton's admonition. "Prevent jamming, oil them well! You'll never get a second chance!"

Under the cover of night we moved out as silently as we came in. The farmer and his wife watched us leave. "May the Virgin be with you!" he said. His woman echoed, "Amen!"

It was nearly midnight when our small band reached the SS concentration. Silently we separated into ten groups of four; each went its designated way. I was frightened but did not dare mention it for fear the others were frightened too. I repeated the instructions over and over. "Place the plastic inside the turrets! Secure it well! Set the fuses at half an hour! Be sure not to attract attention!"

Anton had said, "You must hate his guts, my boy, it will be easier to spill them." But I still wondered if I could pull the trigger when the time came. Mechanically, I prayed things to go well.

It took almost an hour to accomplish our assignment. The tanks were ready to blow. All we had to do was observe and wait, which proved almost as nerve-wracking as installing the charges. Time and again the unsuspecting sentries came within an arm's length of the explosives.

With only six minutes to go, we observed some excitement in the enemy camp. The SS were dragging four men to the guardhouse almost fifty yards away from us, shouting and striking them with rifle butts.

"We've got to create some diversion!" Pola hissed. "The goons got novices."

The "novices" were four of our group.

"What are we waiting for! Let's go!"

Before the SS knew what happened, we were spraying bullets in all directions. But, it took them only moments to organize and return our fire. Anton lay bleeding in the snow, I ran toward him.

"Anton!"

"Go on, get one! Someone betrayed us! Kill the bastards!"

I ran and I killed, hoping all along that the charges would soon go off. The metal in my grip was getting unbearably hot, and I stopped counting my victims. The war was mine now.

In all the confusion the charges went off with a powerful quake. The SS was momentarily dumbfounded. We took advantage of the surprise and retreated, taking the wounded with us. As far as we could tell, there were only seven of us wounded. Three of the group captured by the SS were dead.

Through the dense woods we hurried back toward the farm. Anton and Yossele had to be carried on makeshift stretchers. The triumph of our mission might have been complete were it not for the casualties; nothing short of surgery was going to save Anton.

We stopped for a rest not too far from the farm. Piotr, Franek, and Zbyszek were sent to see if all were clear. They did not notice anything unusual as they approached the yard, but the farmer and his wife did not respond to the three short whistles. Then they saw it. High from the hay loft hung the limp bodies. Not a sound was heard.

"We had guests," Zbyszek whispered to Piotr.

"Wonder if any stayed."

"We'd better find out."

The men went closer to the hanged couple. The bodies were riddled with bullets. On each back, the inscription: "This is our payment to saboteurs."

We knew then we had been betrayed. But by whom?

"We've got to get a decent bed for Anton and Yossele or they'll die," Zbyszek remarked.

"What if the SS come back?" Franek inquired cautiously.

"We'll have to run that risk. They won't be back soon; they got what they came for. I'd like to get the swine who informed!" Zbyszek spat through his teeth and turned to go.

Zbyszek reported his findings to Pola. Intuitively she argued that it was a trap. But Anton was delirious and she decided to go in.

We were in the middle of the yard when the barn gates opened and we faced the barrel of a 3.5 mm. tank cannon.

"Run for cover!" Pola screamed, kneeling in front of the two wounded. We opened fire and tossed a few pineapple grenades which bounced off the tank, but before we were able to cry out, the tank was almost on top of them. Pola jumped out of the way and Anton rolled over under the belly of the vehicle. Yossele was caught across the thighs. Seconds later an explosion shook the tank and set its fuel on fire. Infuriated, we ran screaming toward the burning tank. Menasha jumped on and used his gun to pry open the manhole. He hurled a stick hand grenade inside. None of the four crew members escaped.

Nine freshly dug graves marked the farm yard as we left. It was too high a price for our small victory. Anton's death created a particularly wide gap in our ranks. And Yossele. At least he died with a good pair of boots on his feet. Someone would have to carry the news to his father. He was the last of the four captured by the SS and the secret of the alleged betrayal died with him.

That night Pola contacted headquarters. None of us knew where our instructions originated and we preferred it that way.

"We're moving on to Siedlce!" Pola addressed the group for the first time since the skirmish. She was resolute once again.

"To Siedlce? What for?" the men asked curiously.

"You'll find out when we get there! Prepare to move out!"

I whispered to Roman, "Isn't anyone going to say the Kaddish for the dead?"

"You don't say the Kaddish for a goy!"

"I don't see why not."

"You simply don't, that's all!"

"I'm going to recite it just the same."

"You can't, you're not of age," Menasha remarked.

"If you refuse, I just might!" I repeated stubbornly.

"And how are you going to separate the goyim from our boys?"

"I don't intend to separate anyone."

Menasha prayed. He spoke the solemn words of the age-old supplication and we countered with the customary "amen." He looked at us, "I didn't pray for the dead alone. My words are for us; no one will say the Kaddish for us."

"Don't be absurd. Think of what you're saying, Menasha."

"I am thinking, Roman, and that's exactly what I mean. We are now like *them*. It's their greatest achievement. First they took our homes, then our families. They even eradicated the Jew's capacity to laugh at himself. And now we kill, just as they do."

"Not quite, Menasha. We have not killed the unarmed, the children."

"Give it time, my friend. It will come."

❧

And it came to pass . . .

The deluge continued on,
For the Æsir became wrathful
Even as the darkest Hel,
And brother fought against brother . . .

And it came to pass . . .

The Earth shed bitter tears,
For her children were slain,
And siblings did incest,
And there was no salvation in sight . . .

And the sages mourned . . .

❦ HAYIM

O my son Absalom, my son
my son Absalom!
Would I had died for thee,
O Absalom, my son, my son!
II SAMUEL 19:1

Hayim vaguely remembered Roman's admonition—or was it a blessing? The next thing he heard was Yurek's hushed voice coming at him from the dark.

"Hayim? Is that you, Hayim?"

"It is I," the boy replied, still trembling.

"Over here. Step lively. Over here! . . . Don't be frightened, Hayim."

"I am not frightened."

Yurek sought reassurance in Hayim's composure. They ran.

The Skowrons had tried everything to make him feel at home. There were games, and there were long conversations with Yurek. But Hayim was unable to adjust to the life of a fugitive. He was permitted outdoors only briefly during the night. His days were all marked by fear, vigilance, and confinement.

"Soon, my son, soon you will be free." Mrs. Skowron often tried to encourage the boy. "The Germans are retreating and we ought to be liberated by the advancing Soviets. This will seem only like a dark cloud when it passes."

"Any time in confinement is a long time," Hayim

thought, but he did not speak for fear he would hurt her feelings. He knew how difficult life had become for the Skowrons since his arrival. There were spying, inquisitive eyes everywhere, eyes which are created by wars alone. Hayim would wait. He had learned to wait. He would not jeopardize the security of his benefactors. In his solitude, he wondered about the world.

Even though precautions had been taken, Hayim's presence in the Skowron household could not remain a secret forever. Out for a walk, Yurek was confronted by a group of his friends. "Why can't we come to see you at your place anymore? You always find excuses to keep us out. What's the matter, Yurek?"

"Maybe they're hiding a Jew? Eh, Yurek, maybe you're getting good money for keeping a Jew?"

He swung wildly at them. They respected his fists and ran. At a safe distance they stopped.

"Jew-lover! Jew-protector! Maybe you're one of them! Jude! Jude!"

Yurek stood immobile; none of the accusations stung him more deeply than being paid for Hayim's safety.

During his stay with the Skowrons, Hayim learned to exist in a make-believe world. He hid when there were strangers in the house and listened to the mysterious discussions. The visitors spoke a great deal about politics and the world situation; some of it he did not understand, some of it was too clear.

"Well, another execution this morning on the market-place."

"Who was it this time?"

"Moshkowitz, the tailor, you remember, the one from Ulica Zielna. They discovered his hiding place in the old mikvah."

Hayim wondered how long it would take them to discover him.

"We didn't know he was in hiding," Mrs. Skowron showed surprise. "He was last seen deported with his family."

"Seems like the Bureau discovers things sooner or later," the guest continued. "They say the tailor had a contact providing him with food and necessities. When the contact failed to show up for almost fourteen days, and his provisions had run out, the tailor took the risk. He was seized before turning the corner, by one of 'ours' at that."

"If only Yossele were still here," Hayim thought. "Now there is no one left to say Kaddish for the old tailor."

"We always did have a better nose for detecting Jews than the Gestapo," a second guest remarked with a chuckle.

About a week later, early in the afternoon, Hayim pleaded with Mrs. Skowron to allow him to play in the nearby garden for a while. Yurek interceded for his friend and Mama Skowron yielded against her better judgment. The garden was around the corner and ran directly into the dead-end alley terminating at the old deserted brewery. Hayim had meant all along to visit the mysterious location. He had seen it each day from his window as it waited to be conquered, if only he could conquer himself.

The day seemed ideal for an exploratory excursion. The sun was shining brightly. There was that certain tentative warmth in the air. As he strolled through the garden, Hayim felt at peace. He had made up his mind to leave the Skowrons that night.

"There, there he is!" someone shouted in Lithuanian, and Hayim heard booted footsteps all around.

"Oh, my God, merciful God, they've come for me!"

Across the garden he saw two Gestapo officials and several Lithuanian SS. One SS was interrogating a pedestrian while another, quite by coincidence, looked at Hayim. Hayim turned away and tried to be calm but conditioning prevailed and he ran.

"Jude! Jude! Halt!"

"Verflucht nochmal! Bleib stehen!"

"Stop or I'll shoot!"

Shots resounded through the neighborhood.

"A Jew, a Jew! There he goes!"

Hayim ran straight into the merciless wall of the old brewery. There, panting and urinating down his leg, he tried to pray but no words came. A small crowd gathered to observe the ritual. Those who looked saw an SS reach the boy. It was breathtakingly quiet. The boy fell and was pulled up by the crop of his hair. The SS put the barrel of his Luger to Hayim's head and pulled the trigger.

Hayim is the Hebrew word for "life."

Spring had come. We established our headquarters in an abandoned forester's hut not far from Biala Podlaska—the small town near the Russian frontier.

Our regular reconnaissance revealed that twice weekly, at the Biala Podlaska railway station, freight had to be transferred from trains on the wide gauge Soviet tracks to empty cars waiting on the standard size Polish tracks.

The arrival of the westbound trains was typically punctual. Troops and equipment were transferred quietly during the night and were on their way in a few hours. A Sonderkommando of the elite SS, under the able command of Obersturmbannführer Kurt Willhaus, was charged with the safety of all operations.

It was quite simple to investigate the habits of Kurt Willhaus. Like Himmler whom he emulated and worshiped, Willhaus was a Studienrat by profession. He was honest, exacting, painstakingly punctual, and disarmingly loyal. It goes without saying that he demanded these qualities of his men.

Customarily, a strong detachment of SS was dispatched

moments before the arrival of the westbound trains. The timing was perfect. No sooner did the incoming train whistle sound than the SS appeared at the station to take full charge of operations.

"We'll keep the SS busy while you plant the explosives!" Pola was her energetic self again, as she instructed the four men selected for the mission. "Lay them well, along the tracks on both sides. Give it fifteen minutes to blow after the switchover."

To think that Tuviah, Yussuf, Yaakov, and Pinhas was a sufficient force to do powerful mischief to the German line of communications! Yet it was true. "There is strength in small numbers," Zbyszek remarked. He had inherited Anton's portion of Pola. As her undisputed lover and chief lieutenant, Zbyszek maintained discipline among the men.

"Remember," Zbyszek instructed the departing four men, "the inconspicuous survive the trials of war, because the pursuer seeks relentlessly after the obvious. You must lay your charges carefully. Pressure mines are delicate business."

"Roman, Menasha was right," I whispered, "we build and they destroy. Now we destroy as well. We *are* like them!"

"Don't be a fool. We fight the best way we know how," Roman replied.

"It's not that simple," I insisted. "Seems like everything is crazy and we are at the very center of it!"

"Yes, so?" My brother cut off the discussion.

"Good-bye, Tuviah!"

"Take care, Pinhas!"

The four men left the camp. If they were frightened, they concealed it well.

When the word came to move out, we were ready.

Our four comrades successfully accomplished their mission in Biala Podlaska. While Obersturmbannführer Willhaus deployed a major detachment of his Sonderkommando to

Lukow to pursue us, the German railway link between east and west lay utterly devastated. Even at a distance we could feel the powerful tremor as we eluded the SS.

It was easier, however, to attract the attention of the Führer's elite guard than to get rid of it. The Sonderkommando on our heels, we made our way back to the forest, hoping to reach our comrades.

The meadow stretched out before us. Beyond that the forest, and then our hut.

"Look, Roman," I whispered, although there was no sign of the enemy. "Just like a soccer field."

"Be still now, this is no time to have games on your mind."

"But it is just like old times," I insisted, "all that's missing are the two goals."

"Will you shut up!"

"But look how nice and green it looks."

"If you don't shut your mouth, you might be put to rest there forever!"

Roman was tense. The silence of the meadow and the uncertainty of the distant forest were frightening.

Zbyszek broke the silence. "Let me take a few men across. If they're there, this will get them out. If we make it, you'll follow."

Pola nodded. Without further discussion, Zbyszek motioned several men to follow him. Cautiously, they stalked through the clearing and into the distant line of the trees. Pola gave orders to move out. Suddenly machine guns sounded from where our comrades should have been at that moment. Only isolated side-arm shots were returned. Then, all was still again.

"Let's get out of here!" Pola shouted, but no sooner had our hasty retreat begun when we heard Willhaus across the clearing.

"Lay down your arms! Come out with your hands above

your head! You are surrounded! You don't have a chance!"

A heavy salvo was shot above our heads. We lay still for a moment.

"They want us alive," Roman whispered. "They won't shoot because we're worth more to them alive than dead."

"We can't win the stinking war on our own anyhow," Menasha agreed, "but I'd sure like to see the swastika on the run."

"What are we going to do?" I asked.

"Stay here till nightfall, maybe we can still get out of it our own way . . ."

Menasha was about to continue when Pola suddenly ran toward the invisible enemy, shooting wildly and shouting barely audible abuse. It took only one barrage to fell her. Her fingers convulsively squeezed the final rounds of ammunition as she died.

We were silent. I was reminded of King David's words and thought, "But now she is dead, wherefore should I fast? Can I bring her back again? I shall go to her, but she will not return to me."

No one wept. And none of us said Kaddish. After all, one does not say Kaddish for a shikse.

❧

And it came to pass . . .

The Æsir dispatched emissaries of
Good will, to muster aid for
Balder's release from the bonds of Hel,
That lasting peace may come to reign . . .

And the seers weepingly tell

Of the cunning Loki, whose evil
Schemes have once more foiled the
Æsir's will. The good son was gone
Forever, and darkness befell the earth . . .

And it came to pass . . .

~§~ BUCHENWALD

Let the priests, the ministers of
the Lord,
Weep between the porch and the
altar,
And let them say:
"Spare Thy people, O Lord . . ."
JOEL 2:17

In their classic style the Gestapo, alternating soft and brutal treatment, interrogated us about the sabotage. They hung some, placing signs on the front and back of the victims: "This is what we do to the resistance." But that only made the rest of us more stubborn. Ultimately we might have succumbed had it not been for the electrifying news of the Warsaw uprising.

Preparations for the Final Solution in Warsaw had begun as far back as the 20th of July, 1942, when several companies of the crack SS-Standarte Reinhard Haydrich were transferred there from the extermination camp in Lublin. Every day thereafter ten thousand Jews were transported to the Lublin and Treblinka camps. It had been a relatively simple operation for the experienced SS unit. The Ukrainian SS mercenaries had surrounded the walls of the Warsaw ghetto. The order was then issued from the German military headquarters: "ALL JEWS, MEN, WOMEN, AND CHILDREN, NOT EMPLOYED IN GERMAN WAR INDUSTRY OR

THE CITY ADMINISTRATION, MUST VACATE
THE GHETTO!"

The Jews were allegedly to be taken east in order to
help reconstruct the devastated territories. In his meticulous
manner, the enemy created the impressive office of "SS-
Aussiedlungsstab (the "SS Headquarters for the Transfer of
Population"), in Warsaw under the command of SS-Sturm-
bannführer Hans Brand. He was a quiet, unassuming man.
Each day, quietly and most efficiently, he transported ten
thousand souls out of the Warsaw ghetto to the eastern "Re-
habilitation Areas." Soon, in their stead, ten thousand
shadows returned to the ghetto skies. Those who had seen it
all happen said that soon the sun's rays would not penetrate
the hard core of the returned shadows. They hovered over
the condemned city and spoke eloquently of the futile hopes
of the living.

But it was late. The total ghetto population numbered
into 40,000, mostly children below the age of fifteen, when
the fate of the departed dawned upon the remaining few.
Rumors were heard.

"Their shadows have returned, and we must mourn."

"It is His way of telling us what to do!"

"Blessed be He, amen!"

The Soviet Armies pushed the retreating enemy westward. Soon they would occupy the eastern shore of the
Vistula. Word was sent to their commanding general and he
returned his pledge to aid the rebellion.

Purim had passed, and it was nearly Passover 1943. As
though to commemorate that significant festival, the three
quarreling political youth organizations, the Hashomer
Hatzair, the Mizrahi, and the Hashomer Hadatti, united
under the name of The Jewish Armed Organization in a
secret declaration to resist resettlement. If they were to die,
they vowed to do it with honor.

"Dayenu, it is enough, if we don't make a stand now, we

will be too weak to resist at all," the leaders all agreed. By word of mouth the news to resist spread. There was no Moses to bring plagues on the insidious enemy, nor beautiful Queen Esther to plead the cause of her Warsaw brethren. Few had received legitimate weapons, but the streets were full of war debris. "Even you can throw a rock!" mothers had told their children. "Remember how David slew Goliath with a small rock? This is how we shall all do it, we shall smite our enemy, and the Almighty will guide our arm, blessed be His name!"

"Eine Unverschämtheit! Die verfluchten Hunde!" Sturmbannführer Brand was beside himself. With what audacity these damned dogs dared resist his orders; the very authority relegated to him from the great Führer himself, his praeceptor Germaniae! "We shall show these uncultured swine that we mean to have our orders obeyed!" Herr Brand stumped his polished boots up and down the floor. He would have to call in other units to aid his operation. His superiors would not like this.

"No, I won't!" he shouted, as though to drown his doubts. "We shall proceed ourselves! The front needs every available man! We shall not weaken it! We shall show these pigs behind their stinking walls how superior we really are! Heil Hitler!"

"Heil Hitler!" Came a resounding echo from his subordinates. While Brand was getting ready to move into the ghetto, the people had been warned by couriers to prepare. And when the SS entered the ghetto walls, the insurgents were ready.

An SS detachment under the command of Scharführer Oswald Dukat approached the corner of Nalewki Street, house number 42, opposite Braner's clothing factory. A young man came out of the factory gate and ran toward the leader of the group.

"There, the third yard straight on, there are ten Jews hidden. I saw them with my own eyes. They have weapons!"

The SS followed the young informer as he led them to the indicated yard. Scarcely had they reached it, when the boy suddenly produced a pistol, discharging point blank at the head of Scharführer Dukat. The signal had been given. Shots came from every direction. Hand grenades exploded with much effect and a deafening noise. The young man who had fired the first shot was a Mizrahi fighter, Mordechai Nutkowicz, from the small town of Typin, northwest of Warsaw. Moments after he fired he fell, riddled with SS bullets. But not one of the small enemy detachment left the yard alive. Fights broke out throughout the ghetto. The great battle had begun. Additional forces had to be summoned. The SS withdrew momentarily.

Sturmbannführer Brand was not prepared for the reception he had received. After all, those were inferior people! They dared resist! They would pay for it dearly!

Rumors had it that the departed SS warriors did not return to the ghetto in the form of shadows. They would not mingle with the shadows of an inferior race. Instead, they were all transformed into black knights of Barbarossa, destined to spend eternity at his Valhalla under the granite rock of the Kyffhäuser.

The German Elite SS, hurting from defeat on the Russian front, needed a victory, and it really did not matter over whom. The Warsaw uprising was made to order; a few Jews, hiding out in the ruins of a ghetto, fighting the brave invaders with primordial weapons, and dying the death of an inferior race. Here was the easy victory for the SS as well as a further step in the Final Solution.

There was an uneasy silence during the few days of preparations. The Germans were not taking any chances. All known land and air weaponry was moved into the area. It was a well-coordinated campaign, and needless to say, the insurgence was put down. The ghetto burned in all four corners under constant bombardment.

All took place while the Soviets stood on the eastern

shore of the Vistula, within sight of the annihilation. Time and again, messengers were sent to the commanders of the Soviet forces; each time they returned with renewed hope.

"We are expecting orders from the Supreme Command in Moscow. We will join you soon in your struggle. Hold out! We stand by you!"

And while the "orders" were late in arriving, there were those unwilling to passively witness the slaughter who swam from the eastern shore. They joined the struggle and shared the fate while all appeals for aid were unanswered.

Within fourteen days most of the Jews joined the shadows over the Warsaw ghetto. The punitive SS action was concluded, and a proclamation was issued stating that the Sauberungsaktion, the "cleansing" of the city, had come to a successful conclusion. On that day complete darkness of mourning enveloped the ancient city.

We had learned about the last days of the Warsaw ghetto from the few survivors who were herded into the Lublin camp several weeks later. Everyone ran toward the newly arrived, eager to learn about some relatives or friends who may have been part of the insurgence. We milled around for hours without results.

"See that old man over there?" Roman pointed toward a newly arrived Jew squatting in the corner of the barrack. His clothes were torn to shreds and his head was covered with dirt. "He is only twenty-nine years old."

"I can't believe it!" Menasha exclaimed. "He doesn't look a day younger than sixty-five!"

"That's what I thought, until they told me who he was . . . You're looking at the celebrated violinist Robert Kadetzki. Remember, he played with Uncle Michael's orchestra at the Lazienki Park, the last time we were in Warsaw."

"Yes, I remember. Every time Uncle Michael could, he would wave, and we waved back. But this could not be the same man."

"Yes, little brother, it is."

"They took her from me, they took my Tania, my darling, my life. I shall never see her." There was too much grief to interrupt the wailing man. We listened and squatted near. Finally he told us about the last days of Warsaw and the camp at Treblinka.

"I was separated from my wife," he repeated, "and I never saw her again after the clean-up action began." Kadetzki spoke and there was no indication that he was addressing anyone in particular. When the pain of his experiences carried him back he would press his fist tightly to his temples as though to force out the voices of despair.

"Shortly before the final evacuation, all the sick taken from their homes as well as the hospitals, including the inhabitants of the old-folks home and the children of the orphanage, almost five hundred, were shot or killed by phenol injections." His body swayed back and forth in the fashion of mourners. "I wish I were with them but now I must sit shiva for all of them, I sit shiva for the world which has gone mad!" The man ceased narrating and we waited.

"As a young, strong man, I was given the task of burying the bodies in a mass grave at Okrzej Street. We threw the dead into their grave with their clothes on, but were ordered to search each one for jewelry, gold, and money to turn over to the SS. At the end of it, we were assembled in the old synagogue, and the following day Gestapo chief Wilhelm Badnark ordered some of us to be transported to Treblinka. As for those remaining behind, I can only guess."

Menasha's lips were moving rapidly, and I knew he was saying Kaddish. He recited too fast for us but we caught the last veimru, and we quickly added, "amen."

The train transport was dreadful," the man continued. "We were crammed into the boxcars; children cried and women went insane with grief and worry. The transport arrived at about three o'clock in the afternoon at Arbeitslager Treblinka. From there, the train was pulled off onto a spur and then further into the forest, a distance of about three to five kilometers. And there . . ."

The virtuoso choked and continued to sway back and forth, emitting incoherent, inarticulate sounds. We hoped he would go on and tell us the truth he knew about those we loved, but at the same time, I found myself hoping he would go no further.

"And there hundreds of corpses lay on a clearing. Baggage, clothes, suitcases were strewn among them, everything was in a state of utter confusion. We were driven out of the cars, while German and Ukrainian SS climbed on the roofs and shot into the crowd. Men, women, and children waltzed in their own blood. Wild screaming and crying filled the air. Suddenly the shooting subsided, and those who were not shot or wounded were herded through an open gate into a barbed wire area. I was sent with a group of others to clean the cars and pile up the corpses in an orderly fashion in the enclosed area. A bottle of Schnapps in the one hand, clubs or pistols in the other, the SS forced us to work rapidly. The memory of children held by their feet and slung against tree trunks still haunts me. We were beaten time and again, on the slightest pretext, for the benefit of the SS commander, his staff, and the ever-present photographic equipment.

"We received little food, although we were forced to do the most demanding work. Each day two or three transports arrived. We kept ourselves alive on what food we could find in the baggage of the condemned.

"Many transports arrived with only corpses. No wounds could be seen but their bodies were all entwined and their skin was blue. Somehow, some three to five-year-old children survived the gassing, although deaf, with bewildered eyes and unable to speak. We could not hide them very long before the SS found them. Transports also arrived with mostly children, or old people. For hours they waited on a siding, to be 'liquidated' by machine gun fire.

"From Treblinka, groups of two to five hundred men were regularly driven naked through the forest. Placed in rows and holding hands as if engaged in a macabre dance, they were ordered to the rim of the dredged graves. The SS made it a sport to kill those unfortunates by a shot in the neck. As the men fell, the guards would kick them into the graves and argue about who had kicked the victims the farthest.

"There was also a small house built not far from the forest. Outside it looked no different from any house, but inside it was the finest tile. On the trail leading to that house there was a sign 'TO THE BATHS.' Another sign instructed the newcomers to deposit their valuables, all currency, and neatly bundled clothes at the reception window. Punishment was meted out quite generously to persons delinquent in neatness.

"From that time forth the new arrivals were no longer shot. The Germans, in their ingenious and orderly manner, had discovered a less expensive, more efficient way leading to the Final Solution: gassing.

"Once again, I was selected, among others, to remove the cremated remains of the unfortunates. We were given no food and continued to survive on the food articles we had found in the belongings of the victims.

"I died when I saw the boxcars arrive, and I died when they were unloaded. I died over and over again, and now, I am here to mourn the shadows which are all around us. They won't let me rest, no matter how I plead. My eyes have seen too much, and even now they see it over and over again, even in their utmost exhaustion. I pray death comes and until it comes, I must sit and mourn—the shadows command that."

His listeners were stunned to the very core of their meager existence. During the virtuoso's narration many had gathered, each wishing that perhaps a name or an event would be mentioned to renew hope. With the last sentence of the

222

narrative, they silently dispersed, each to his own corner. Their eyes were dry, for they had seen too much.

"It's gone, it's all gone now," I muttered to myself as I walked away, "and there is nothing left."

In keeping with the mandates of a superior people, and faithful to the precepts of the Führer, the Gestapo hierarchy responded to a most pressing problem besetting the Third Reich in its impressive program against the decadence of the world: an acute shortage of labor in the war factories. The planners, in their inimitable and boundless ingenuity, created a labor-providing plan that was compatible with the ambitious aims of the Final Solution. Soon the acronym of the institution for the "liquidation of every real or suspected enemy of the National Socialist State" became a household word throughout the world, the K.Z.

There were three stages of K.Z., and we contemplated our chances on the way to interment. We had hoped for an Arbeitslager, that being the mildest form of punishment. However, we were quite willing to settle for the Straflager, a more severe punitive, hard-labor camp.

"Buchenwald! Buchenwald! We are on our way to Buchenwald!"

The rumor spread throughout the entire transport. We had heard of those types of K.Z. also. Good humoredly, the Gestapo nicknamed them Knochenmühlen, "bone-grinders."

As we were relentlessly carried nearer our destination, we realized that soon we would be among the worst conglomerate of humanity. The "habitual" Jew, according to the Nuremberg "oracle," was equal only in social stature to the habitual criminal, the incorrigible homosexual, the Gypsy, defiant clergy of all faiths, and the political opposition to the

223

Reich. The Jew, it was said, possessed the combined qualities of all these undesirable social elements, and rumor had it that only on rarest occasions did a Knochenmühle inmate leave alive.

K.Z. Buchenwald was situated appropriately on a high elevation in the midst of a splendid forest. It was surrounded by barbed wire which carried an intense electrical charge and was reinforced every seventy-five meters by a guard-tower bearing an expertly manned machine gun. The weapon was placed on a turret for better maneuverability. Each tower was also equipped with large spotlights to illuminate the area between the barracks and the barbed wire during all hours of the night.

The last stop. The K.Z. Only half of the inmates who had left Lublin were still alive. The SS guards had no trouble at all persuading the remainder to form a column of fours. A few incoherent shouts, a few well-aimed blows, and the men did as ordered. The thought of survival alone kept us going. We stayed together, Roman, Menasha, and I, and hoped to continue together.

The entrance to the camp was a large fort-like gate flanked by two large towers. As our column approached, we saw the inscriptions above the gate: *Recht oder Unrecht mein Vaterland!* ("Right or wrong—my country!") and *Arbeit macht frei!* ("Work makes one free.") We paid little attention to the first but the second renewed hope. "After all," I thought, "as long as we do our job, we may get out of this yet."

From the gate all the way to the first row of barracks there was an empty, barren space, the Appellplatz. Muddy because of the recent rains, the red clay promised to be quite dry and dusty. The long, low barracks stretched out across the vast distance.

"I hope they allow me to keep the photos," I whispered to Roman.

"Don't worry about the photos at a time like this," was his hushed reply. But I did worry; there was not much more left of us.

As we marched into the Appellplatz, it was early afternoon. There were SS guards, Croatian and Ukrainian mercenaries, and our own Kapos; they were all there, as if anticipating an eventful afternoon.

"What's a Kapo, Roman?" I noticed an inscription on the breastpocket of one of the zebra-clad overseers, armed with a billy club.

"Comes from the Italian *il capo*, which amounts to the same as 'head,' or 'superior.' All I know is that he is an internee who does camp duty in return for a little more food and a little less ill-treatment."

"And the bastard gives the rough treatment to the rest of us," Menasha interjected.

"Isn't this place near Weimar?"

"Yes," he sneered, "Weimar was once the site of German Classicism—Goethe, Schiller, even Beethoven lived there for a while."

"You there! Schweinehund!" an SS guard shouted in our direction. I shrunk into the column of men around me, fearing he had addressed me. I was relieved, however momentarily, to note that I was not the object of his attention.

The SS man rushed over, clubbing everyone in his wake. He grabbed Menasha by the lonely earlock which had somehow managed to slip out from under his tight cap, and pulled him out of our ranks. Blow upon blow followed. He was ordered to kneel and undress.

"Pray to your God!"

To our utter disbelief, the tormentors stood round the

kneeling Hasid and proceeded to urinate onto his face, hair, and on the whole kneeling picture of piety. Menasha kept on praying. The guards suffered hiccups from violent laughter.

Once again there were shadows everywhere. We knew then that there were things to come which would make the past seem trivial. And we knew then that there were degrees of evil as there were degrees of life.

By the mere caprice of a guard, Menasha might have been killed, but a Kapo interfered.

"Herr Sturmbannführer, may I point out that this is a healthy specimen. Leave him to us. We'll teach him the right ways."

"You're right!" The officer slapped his thighs. "Let him go! . . . And you better pray to your Kapo from now on! It was he who saved your miserable hide!" The guards roared with laughter, but Menasha returned to our ranks. He was bruised and bleeding, but alive.

"We have to hand it to our Kapo. He certainly wields a lot of power around these parts," I whispered to Roman.

"Thank God, and God alone, blessed be He," Menasha mumbled. As we moved on, he walked proudly and without a sign of fatigue.

"We must go on waiting and praying," he said.

"Wait and pray for what?" I asked.

"For another miracle."

"A miracle?"

"Yes, like the one that just happened."

"You might wish tomorrow that it hadn't."

"Never say that, my boy. If they break your will to live, you're through."

"Now we are to wait for another miracle! Our God left us long ago, Menasha. He sent us the shadows of the dead instead, and they are powerless."

"This is blasphemy! Tonight you say the Sh'ma a hundred times!

"God has forgotten our language, and I have almost forgotten His."

"Then, you must remember once again and ask forgiveness."

"Aren't you a little mixed up, Menasha? It is He who should ask forgiveness! And this is quite the right place for a din Torah! And may all the shadows be our witnesses!"

"You don't know what you're saying! You're mad. His ways may seem strange to us at times, but they are always just!"

"See here, Menasha . . ." We had arrived at the building with a large sign over its entrance and my heart almost stopped: *BAD und DESINFEKTION!* "The same trick they used in Treblinka."

There it was: the windowless room. We deposited our clothing and all our belongings with the inmates who inspected the mouth for golden teeth and the rectum for money or valuables.

Without realizing it, I recited the Sh'ma from the moment we had entered the "delousing" area and prayed through the complete ritual. The instruments used to shave every hair on our bodies were not of the best quality. The torn skin bled profusely, especially in delicate places where the dull steel broke into flesh. I continued the prayer as we were told to submerge, one at a time, in a large container of strong disinfectant. It burned intensely, and we ran toward the showers anticipating the flow of warm water to wash off the burning effects. But it was ice cold. "At least it isn't gas!" I thought as I continued the Sh'ma.

The striped inmates' clothing, Dutch wooden shoes, and one blanket per person were evidence that we were to go on living; temporarily, at least. We were given a new identity. From then on, I was 1461, the legacy left me by the former owner of my uniform. I prayed a little faster when I noticed the three bullet-sized holes in my jacket. But as we were driven toward the barracks, I was too busy holding onto my loose trousers and keeping the wooden shoes from getting stuck in the mud to think about the holes in my jacket.

Two thousand inmates were herded into a barrack, a space which at best could normally accommodate five hundred men. We knew from experience to select the uppermost berth to avoid being stepped on in the future.

The Kapo rendered a prepared welcome lecture on the merits of individual obedience and camp discipline. "We are all in the same boat here; if you lose your bread ration, you're dead. If some bastard steals it from you, he just as much as kills you. Respect the property of others and you won't get hurt. We catch you stealing and *you're* dead."

I mourned the confiscated family photos; soon, however, the mental pictures became stronger. I wondered how long that would last.

"Do you still remember Mama?" I kept asking Roman. "And Felusia? Tell me, how did they both look on the day of their departure?"

My brother would go on, endlessly describing the features of both. It became a daily ritual.

"Let's talk about them each day," I begged, "so we won't forget how they both looked."

"We shall, little brother, as long as we're together, we shall talk."

The thought that we might be separated had not entered my mind. But there existed that possibility. Each day there were transports leaving Buchenwald to various other camps. The SS was particularly keen on separating families once they had learned their identities.

"Why couldn't we have become members of the great German community. We might have been victors today."

"Because . . . because 'Point Four' of the NSDAP program distinctly states that 'only a member of the race can be a citizen. A member of the race can only be one who is of

German blood, without consideration of creed.' Consequently, no Jew can be a member of the race. They drilled that into every one of us in the sixth grade. I guess they need the barrier; they've always been out of place in the world. Who knows," Roman shrugged. "Maybe now they feel secure."

"But, what do *we* have to do with all that?"

"They need us, little brother, for contrast. That's why they keep us. It's all in here." Roman reached under his shirt and produced a small pocket-edition of *Mein Kampf*.

"Where did you get that?"

"I found it the other day on the Appellplatz. One of the guards must have lost it."

"Let's destroy it, Roman," I pleaded. "It can cause a lot of trouble."

"Oh, we will, don't get excited."

That night we both had the satisfaction of making symbolic use of the pages, but even as toilet paper, contact with them proved disagreeable.

From the first day at the camp, we had ample opportunity to acquaint ourselves with the powers of the Kapo. At the slightest provocation, he would let a "delinquent" stand for hours facing the wall, or he would make him perform knee-bends until the prisoner dropped, only to be kicked unconscious. The amazing phenomenon was that although some of the smashes landed on areas which would customarily bleed, there was no blood whatsoever.

There was an element of uniformity within the very instability of our existence: the inevitable but gradual turn for the worse. The monotony of suffering. If ever there was a time ripe for the arrival of a Messiah, it was then. The people prayed secretly. The gods of our overseers were jealous gods, and anyone caught worshiping alien gods joined the swelling ranks of the shadows. But even that was a type of deliverance.

During the first weeks of our stay in Buchenwald, all newcomers were ordered to memorize the camp song, *O Buchenwald*. On occasion, the order was shouted.

"Sing, you damn pigs! Sing!"

The inmates sang as best they could. They sang with fear, the fear of those expecting the unexpected.

"Louder! Louder! Till your putrid lungs burst open!"

The melody was sung to the usual marching tempo and was quite easy to follow. The overseers shouted insults and laughed with delight.

Wenn der Tag erwacht . . .*
When the day awakes,
Before the sun can smile,
The columns march forth
To the daily toil
Into the twilight of morning.
And the forest is black, but the sky is red,
And we carry along scarcely little bread
And deep in our hearts there's worry.
  Oh, Buchenwald, I cannot forget you,
  My destiny you are!
  He who has left you, can only fathom
  How wonderful 'tis to be free.
  Oh, Buchenwald, we don't bewail or cry,
  No matter what our fate may be:
  Despite all that, we shall say "yes" to life,
  Because the day will come, we shall be free!
  We shall say "yes" to life,
  Because the day will come, we shall be free!
The night is hot,

* See Appendix.

And my girl is far,
And the wind sings soft
How much I love her,
If only she remained faithful!
And the stones are hard, but firm is our step,
And we carry along our picks and spades
And deep in our hearts there's love.
   Oh, Buchenwald . . . (refrain)
Yet the nights are brief
And the days are long—
And a song resounds
That was sung at home:
No one will take away our courage!
Keep in step, my friend, be without fear,
For we carry the will to live in our blood
And deep in our hearts there's faith!
   Oh, Buchenwald . . . (refrain)

Breathlessly we shouted the song in dissonant, distorted voices as we passed in "review" before the assembled SS. They threw insults at us, the living shadows, and requested countless hours of entertainment without realizing that for many the song had become a source of strength.

Nothing, however, seemed to be able to lift the spirits of Menasha. He had never truly recovered from his initiation into the camp, and was broken in body and spirit. It seemed that his courage had vanished with his earlocks.

One night he was in the middle of the evening services. It was forbidden to openly organize minyans, but the Hasidim overcame that obstacle. By word of mouth they agreed upon a time for the worship. Then, when the hour struck, each man to himself, wherever he was and regardless of what he was doing, would pray. Initiated into the holy ritual, they knew full well when to sound the "amen" during the Kaddish.

"I couldn't stand up to recite the Kaddish, dear God, forgive me but I couldn't," Menasha muttered. "Whatever the Almighty wills, I shall accept," he said softly and then added, "blessed be He." I knew then that the evening services had ended.

In Menasha, I saw living proof that every man has a breaking point; that one day something within him cries out in pain. He clings to life, hopes for better times, hates his tormentors. And one day, like lightning, there is the irrevocable thought that there might never be an answer to this desperation.

After several months of camp existence it became obvious that Menasha's God intended to relieve the young Hasid of his suffering, despite our efforts to keep him alive. By then, Menasha could seldom leave his "bed." Fortunately, we had no work details and we did our best to cover for him at the daily Appell. But we realized that such a situation could scarcely last.

Each day the Blockälteste shouted his usual, *Raus, zum Appell!* The narrow barrack doors vomited the mass of men onto the street. They formed columns of eights and marched in an orderly, mechanical fashion down to the Appellplatz. In the dusk of the morning fog which had scarcely risen from the ground, we were illumined by the spotlights on the sentry towers. Thousands of zebra-clad, sad-faced "Musulmans" trotted sullenly, miserable, not alive and not dead, some singing, others silent, others still doing the "frog-jump" or the "goose-quack," each humoring their superiors, whose desires were as variable as camp life itself.

"Who is it going to be this time?"

We stood shivering in the cool morning air, subjected to the endless headcounts and the abrupt work orders.

"Hope they don't call Menasha!"

"What's taking them so long?"

"They must have called a missing number. We're in for it!"

On occasions, it would take the Kapos and the Blockälteste literally hours before the missing number could be located, at times ill, more often dead, seldom attempting to hide. Hence, in order to prevent these prolonged searches, the inmates themselves would see that the ill and the half-dead participated in the Appell. The dead who were discovered in time were carried outside, stacked neatly in front of the barracks, and accounted for.

Moments after the search had begun, we observed a great deal of excitement near Block 6–A. The missing inmate was located there, dead. He had dared to die before the Appell and the enemy was infuriated. He was tossed onto a heap of skin-covered bones in front of the barracks. Time had fused him into the shadows, to hover eternally above the domain of the enemy.

"I am frightened, Roman, I am frightened because all this does not impress me any longer. It's all the same. Repetitious and nauseating."

He nodded as a sign of understanding. Roman was becoming too weak to speak. It was a gradual, but inevitable change. Sooner or later it was expected of all of us.

"We've got to do something about Menasha or he'll die, Roman."

"Wish I knew what."

"Do you think we ought to pray?"

"Perhaps."

"Menasha says it'll help."

"I am sure it helps, in a way, but . . . I can't . . ."

"What else is left?"

"We'll figure something. We have before."

"Yes, but there is no place we can go from here. We are closed in and the more we curse him, the stronger the enemy becomes."

"Then perhaps we ought to wish our enemies well, little brother?" For a moment, there was a touch of the old humor.

"It's all so unreal, Roman. All of this. You and I,

Menasha, here struggling to please the enemy, or to stay out of his way; refusing to die. It cannot really be happening."

"I, too, expect to awaken any moment, yet waking could never be like this."

The Appell had ended and we lined up to receive our "food" ration for the day; a crust of moldy bread, not over two hundred grams in weight, and a bowl of putrid slush with an occasional turnip.

No sooner had we settled at the long table to eat than the Blockältese was heard reporting: "Attention! Block 364, Wing B, 245 inmates eating!" An ambitious Scharführer decided this was a good time for inspection.

"What? You pigs! You are not under the table yet!"

The bowls were abandoned, benches flew to the side, men scrambled one over the other. But there were always some who could not find refuge under the crowded tables, and they became the whipping boys of the amused enemy.

This was just another game, and they varied with the mood of our gods. At times we would be ordered out of the barracks to stand on our heads in the snow. Occasionally the Kapos would raid the barracks to confiscate blankets they themselves had sold to the inmates at high prices. Those who protested were beaten to unconsciousness. As a result of the beating, the victim's need for the blanket was usually over.

Sporadically men attempted to escape, but even that amused the enemy. Shooting a prisoner attempting to escape earned the SS a furlough and a citation, at times even a promotion. Their diligence was such that soon the inmates learned to forsake these ideas. This, however, was obviously contrary to the SS best interest, so rumors of successful escapes were spread by informers. Again inmates unsuccessfully attempted the impossible. Thereafter, even the most optimistic were silent. But, once again, this threatened to rob the enemy of his favorite pastime. In cooperation with willing Kapos, it was arranged that at certain hours of the night victims were to be delivered to the zone between the gate and the wire to die while "escaping." This game was the best for both worlds. The enemy had his reward and those who could no longer bargain for life had an "escape."

By early 1944 Allied air raids had become a common occurrence in all of the Führer's Germany. Weimar, only seven kilometers from the camp, was not immune to the systematic onslaught. At the very outset of these "atrocities perpetrated on the innocent people of Germany," the Nazi propaganda machinery attempted to minimize the Allied war effort. But the mountains of debris grew, and the disrupted life of the civilian population spoke much louder than all the propaganda organs combined.

For the inmates of Buchenwald, the Allied raids meant street cleaning in the city of Weimar. Each morning, following the roll call, hundreds of inmates were marched downhill to the cradle of culture. Each night, the march uphill was lightened with the expectation of another bombardment. The planes came and we rejoiced.

"Menasha, do you hear? Have courage! We are nearing the end! Our Gods are on the march! Menasha, your prayers have been answered!"

"The Almighty is merciful, blessed be He!" was all Menasha would mutter, as he continued to worship.

Menasha had partially recovered his strength. We were able to share with him some potatoes or vegetables we occasionally unearthed from a cellar of a destroyed home in Weimar. Each time, the Hasid celebrated the unexpected nourishment with a sheheheyanu, and partook only after a faithful recitation of the proper blessing.

On the ninth day of our customary excursions, our

column wound its way through the debris of the devastated city, past the many onlookers. Some stood by passively, others heaped curses upon us as the cause of their misfortune; still others hurled stones as well as abuses.

"How different it might have been, had I come this way another time, as a free man. Who knows," I thought to myself. Just then, the overseer's whip caught my back and I returned to reality.

The humiliating defeats on the home front spurred our overseers on to new "games" for their own amusement. One was being performed on the crossroad not far from our work party.

A group of Jews and Russians were working there under the personal supervision of SS Scharführer Franz Kolehr—a civil engineer before the war—clearing a distance essential to city traffic. Kolehr was meticulous, demanding, and "playful." The work was backbreaking even for strong men, but for the half-starved . . . only fear kept them going. Kolehr singled out a Jew whose strength was dwindling.

"You there, Jude, come over here! Say your last prayers and dig, you are going to die!"

The Jew, Mendel Pototzky from Siedlce, dug and Kolehr ordered one of the Russians to bury the Jew alive.

"Refuse, will you! You dog! We shall see if the Jew does the same! Get in the grave yourself! Schnell!"

Pototzky was ordered to cover the Russian with earth, which he did, hoping to exonerate himself. Moments later only the head of the Russian remained visible and Kolehr stopped the proceedings. He waited while the man struggled out of the grave. Then, he ordered Pototzky to occupy the vacated grave.

"Pray, Jew, pray fast. Let's see the power of your God!" Kolehr laughed. "Now, Rusky, it's your turn."

Pototzky recalled with bewilderment that practically every corner of the old Siedlce shul was filled with the many tzeddakahs of his ancestors; their kovet was imprinted on the old walls and stained-glass windows. The glory of his family had passed with the destruction of the venerable walls, but as long as he lived, God was reminded of the kovet, blessed be His name. Pototzky wanted to live.

The grave filled slowly but relentlessly, and soon the moving surface of the debris was the only indication of Pototzky.

"Stump, Rusky, stump!" Kolehr called excitedly, jumping up and down on the fresh grave until all motion ceased. The Russian turned away, nauseated, and the remaining inmates worked in a frenzy to avoid the challenging spirit of their master. Moments later two of the men were ordered to dig up Pototzky's body. They worked quickly, hoping their comrade might yet be alive. In their haste, one of the men tore the buried man's face in half with his spade. It did not matter, Pototzky was dead. There was no one left to remind God of the kovet. Only strangers and the shadows.

With camp existence, the civilized half of man gradually disappeared and speech patterns changed. Words of courtesy and politeness sounded as strange as promises of a better future. We searched for a purpose to justify our struggle and spent our days fearfully contemplating the shadows of death.

It was impossible to enjoy a tree or an isolated flower. But we were frequently gathered on the immense Appellplatz to witness our gods shed sentimental tears over Wagner as played by undernourished inmates. And we stumbled through the knee-deep snow, frequently losing our wooden shoes on the way to the "concert," holding on to one another for support.

"How can they shed tears to the sound of music!" Roman remarked, while we stood freezing and the SS men wept.

"And they seem to enjoy it, don't they?" I said in disbelief, for I recognized the great paradox among the gods of the camp. The interest in art was maintained in the midst of incessant inhumanity.

And when Christmas came, our gods presented themselves in their very best uniforms. They sang the beautiful verses of the nostalgic "O Tannenbaum" to the accompaniment of the orchestra, even as our own entrails deteriorated and many of the inmates lay in their own excreta, their existence shrouded by an everlasting stupor.

❦

And it came to pass . . .

*In his frightful struggle to end the
Æsir's rule, Loki enlisted monstrous
Forces; Serpents writhed in the seas,
Giants raged supreme . . .*

And woe has come to the Æsir . . .

*And Odin fell, and most of his offsprings
Died. And Frigg succumbed, seeing her
Husband's sad demise. Yet monsters fell,
Struck by Æsir's blazing sword and mighty arm . . .*

And it came to pass . . .

∙◈∙ REBORN

The hand of the Lord was upon me,
and the Lord carried me out in a spirit,
and set me down in the midst of the valley,
and it was full of bones;
and He caused me to pass by them round about,
and, behold, there were very many
　　in the open valley;
and, lo, they were very dry.

And He said unto me: "Son, of man,
　　can these bones live?"
And I answered: "O Lord God,
　　Thou knowest."
Then He said unto me: "Prophesy over
　　these bones, and say unto them:
O ye dry bones, hear the word of the Lord:
Thus saith the Lord God unto these bones:
Behold, I will cause breath to enter into
　　you, and ye shall live.
And I will lay sinews upon you,
And will bring up flesh upon you,
　　and cover you with skin,
　　and put breath in you,
　　and ye shall live;
and ye shall know that I am the LORD."
EZEKIEL 37: 1–6

On June 6, 1944, at 0935 hours, a communiqué (No. 1) was issued by Supreme Headquarters, Allied Expeditionary Force.

UNDER THE COMMAND OF GEN. EISENHOWER, ALLIED NAVAL FORCES, SUPPORTED BY STRONG AIR FORCES, BEGAN LANDING ALLIED ARMIES THIS MORNING ON THE NORTHERN COAST OF FRANCE.

Allied planes took off from airfields in France. The French were jubilant, and their cry was picked up in every corner of suppressed Europe. Its echo reverberated in the most remote corners of the slave camps, injecting renewed hope. The enemy broadcasts marked a conspicuous absence of the Führer's hoarse voice. Nevertheless, the ulcerous supremacy of the swastika continued stubbornly in the confines of the barbed wire fence.

"Do you hear them, Menasha? Do you hear? Feel the earth tremble!"

In his partial stupor Menasha did not realize that we had long since ceased our clean-up excursions to Weimar. Even the enemy knew that no human effort could conceal the havoc created by the Allied bombardments.

"We must survive, Roman, we must do all we can to survive," I said, as the earth trembled under the impact of the falling explosives.

"We will," Roman responded weakly. "Can you hear them, Menasha?"

Menasha turned toward us and spoke with deliberate slowness. "No one survives war . . . the song of the ghetto ends with the Maarev, hash-kee-vay-noo . . . 'Put to rest again' . . . We must all pray that we may be 'put to rest again.' . . . Pray with me."

We could not refuse a dying man. We prayed; at first only to humor the Hasid and then for strength. Joining in the mystical bond of the condemned, we held onto the last vestige of humanity left us.

"Gotenyu, dear God, help us, we have tried and failed. Love made us weak and humor made us seem unreal. We hoped for salvation and the enemy turned our hope to hate. And now, dear God, help us to gain all those things we are unable to attain without You! Lift up the curse from us, for we have been sufficiently punished for our misdeeds, yea, even for the transgressions of our sinful fathers and our fathers' ancestors. Open up the gates of forgiveness, O Merciful God, and be no longer the God of vengeance!"

Forgotten prayers returned to our lips and we went on, in our new strength, inventing new prayers, stronger than the sounds of turmoil.

"Raus, zum Appell!"

The commanding voice of the Blockälteste brought us back to reality and drove us to the Appellplatz, where SS brass were gathered in their finest regalia. Kapos ran back and forth shouting orders, and we soon became aware that events would disrupt the monotony of camp life.

"Achtung!" the Kapo shouted, and a group of SS officers approached the rostrum.

"The Commandant! The supreme god himself!" A murmur went through the vast ranks of men. One of the Commandant's entourage stepped forward.

"Silence! The numbers I will read will all step forward and form ranks of fours in front of the rostrum! There will be no talking in the ranks! Act quickly and you will avoid punishment! Step out lively when your number is called!"

When all the block numbers had been called, Roman and Menasha were on the mysterious roster. Only my number had not been called out.

"What shall we do Roman? Don't leave me here. O God, don't let them do this to us . . . please God . . ."

Suddenly, Menasha tore off my jacket and placed his own on my shoulders.

"Take it and go with God. I haven't much time and you two belong together."

In the next few moments our group was driven by the guards and Kapos through the vast Appellplatz toward the railroad ramp. It was like running from Sodom; we did not look back.

"May God be with you too, Menasha my friend, until we meet again." I whispered, more to myself than anyone in particular, "Please, God, do not be too preoccupied to have witnessed Menasha's supreme tzeddakah."

We traveled six days and seven nights, closed in the customary boxcars. We did not complain, for the renewed hardships were not nearly so bad as separation from each other would have been. "After all, it is only fair. One must be prepared to pay for every blessing," I thought to myself.

On the seventh morning our transport arrived. The sliding doors were pushed aside, and we faced our new masters—men in their sixties and young boys in their teens, wearing loosely fitting Wehrmacht uniforms and wielding somewhat antiquated weapons. Shouting orders, they attempted to appear fierce.

"The Führer is desperate. This is not his old team," I remarked as we were marched toward the distant barracks.

"You may be right, Wilek, let's hope you're right."

"I know I'm right, there are no shadows in the sky."

"Give it time, little brother, these novices will prove themselves worthy."

"They appear harmless enough."

"You should have learned by now not to be fooled by appearances."

"But, I only thought . . ."

242

"That's when you must keep up your guard—when things seem harmless, that's when the worst comes."

"I understand . . . I wonder how Menasha is. What do you think, Roman, how is he, what's going to happen to him?"

"Worry about yourself, little brother. You can't help him. He knew what he was doing." Roman made an effort to sound harsh but I knew.

"But was it right to accept?"

"Who can tell? Who knows what waits for us either."

"Am I less selfish because all is uncertain!"

"Stop it. Menasha has faith. He wished it this way. Accept things as they are."

The matter was closed as far as Roman was concerned, and eventually I too managed to convince myself that it was decreed by the Almighty, blessed be He.

Kolditz was the name of the new camp, and we again became part of the enemy war effort. Quickly and efficiently we were taught to produce the antitank weapons and missiles to kill our allies.

Kolditz was thirty kilometers from Borna, in Saxony, on the crossroads between Leipzig and Dresden. In better days this had been the center of the world-renowned Meissner china, a commodity discontinued with the conversion of the factory into a war apparatus. There was no end to the enemy's ingenuity.

"We are only a few days away from home, Roman, so very close to home."

"Indeed we are. It must mean something; there must be a reason for which we were brought this close to home."

"What do you mean?"

"It can only signify one thing, little brother. Our lives will be spared, home is near and the shadows are close by. Just a while longer, we must hold out a little longer."

"I don't know, Roman, I don't know if I can."

"We are too close to give up now! You must!"

"I'll try, I'll try."

New transports of workers were arriving daily from all parts of Germany. Inmates from Dachau, Belsen, even Auschwitz. Among them were numerous deserters from the Axis forces; Italians were by far greatest in numbers. SS reinforcements also came, and the old and the very young wardens were soon replaced by professionals.

With the new arrivals, food distribution had reached critical dimensions. There was no bread at all left, and none was incoming. We were fed only once daily an ersatz brew which only remotely resembled soup. Soon, we learned to juggle our turn in the food line, to be there when the foreman's ladle went right to the bottom of the vat, fishing out the precious residue of bone fragments and turnips.

"What I wouldn't give for a juicy piece of steak," someone remarked, "even if it were horse meat, why, I'd give five years of my life for such a treat."

"What five years?" came from across the table.

I glanced up at Roman and he looked at me meaningfully, although the old sparkle was almost gone. His face was drawn and his eyes, deeply set in their sockets, were circled by the shadows of death. In his face I saw the reflection of my own.

The following evening, quite by coincidence, I passed near the kitchen moments before feeding time. The steaming vats were on a table, with no one guarding them. Quickly, I reached deep into the nearest vat, my arm was elbow deep in the boiling substance but totally insensitive to the heat. I thought only of the rare fragments of bones, perhaps even a particle of meat, of running joyfully to my brother with the precious finds tucked safely under my blouse. That night we slept while others waked in hunger, and we forgot the feeling of guilt and remorse.

Quite by coincidence, too, we had discovered a way to

244

forget our plight temporarily and use whatever remnants of energy and imagination were left. For months, both Roman and I worked the only two presses on the assembly line which manufactured the firing-pin of the Panzerfaust. Then it came to me.

"What would happen if we bend the metal a bit in the proper places?"

"The mechanism will not fire," Roman repeated solemnly. He stopped what he was doing and looked at me. "You know what will happen if we are discovered? Only you and I, little brother, this is our project."

"This will be for Mother and Felusia, and Grandfather and Grandmother . . ."

"And for Nora and Hayim . . ."

"And all the children of Warsaw . . ."

". . . for all who died al Kiddush hashem . . ."

Months went by and when we were about to falter, we were uplifted by the singular humor of our conspiracy. We visualized scores of enemy antitank crews trying to fire their bazookas without results, and we were glad to be part of the resistance again.

Christmas of 1944 came and passed. There was no voice of the chief god ringing out with "nächste Weihnachten sind Wir zu Hause"; there were only impassioned pleas from the masters, unaccustomed as they were to pleading, for the continued loyalty of the German Volk.

Three major gods met at Yalta to decree the fate of the enemy on February 10–17, 1945. After long deliberations, the following joint communique was issued:

WE HAVE CONSIDERED AND DETERMINED THE
MILITARY PLANS OF THE THREE ALLIED POWERS

FOR THE FINAL DEFEAT OF THE COMMON EN-
EMY. THE MILITARY STAFFS OF THE THREE
ALLIED POWERS HAVE MET DAILY THROUGHOUT
THE CONFERENCE. THESE MEETINGS HAVE BEEN
MOST SATISFACTORY FROM EVERY POINT OF
VIEW AND HAVE RESULTED IN CLOSER COORDI-
NATION OF THE MILITARY EFFORTS OF THE
THREE ALLIES THAN EVER BEFORE. THE FULLEST
INFORMATION HAS BEEN INTERCHANGED. THE
TIMING, SCOPE, AND COORDINATION OF NEW AND
EVEN MORE POWERFUL BLOWS TO BE LAUNCHED
BY OUR ARMIES AND AIR FORCES INTO THE HEART
OF GERMANY FROM EAST, WEST, NORTH, AND
SOUTH HAVE BEEN FULLY AGREED AND PLANNED
IN DETAIL. OUR COMBINED MILITARY PLANS
WILL BE MADE KNOWN ONLY AS WE EXECUTE
THEM, BUT WE BELIEVE THAT THE VERY CLOSE
WORKING PARTNERSHIP AMONG THE THREE
STAFFS ATTAINED AT THIS CONFERENCE WILL
RESULT IN SHORTENING THE WAR. NAZI
GERMANY IS DOOMED. THE GERMAN PEOPLE
WILL ONLY MAKE THE COST OF THEIR DEFEAT
HEAVIER TO THEMSELVES BY ATTEMPTING TO
CONTINUE A HOPELESS RESISTANCE.

The Soviet offensive westward through Poland gained
momentum with the conclusion of the Crimea Conference,
and the excitement among the inmates was beyond measure.
Suddenly our greatest foe was time itself. Each day we listened secretly to the Allied broadcasts with one prayer;
"Dear God, sustain us a bit longer, give us strength to endure

a few more days, only a few days, dear God; after all, what is a few days in the course of Your Creation?"

"They're on the run, the swastika is decomposing, little brother, we must endure!"

"It's ironic, isn't it, Roman, that now the enemy and we are fighting for the same thing."

"How do you mean, little brother?"

"We both fight for time."

Some nights we would revel about the past and things to come, remembering how it used to be. I could almost feel how it was to lie in bed whispering to Roman.

"Remember, we used to hate school, and books, and teachers, and learning . . ."

"I guess I do, vaguely . . ."

"I should never complain about learning again, I promise."

"I won't complain either," Roman repeated halfheartedly.

"And the food, remember how we used to have our likes and dislikes about that?"

"Give me a sackful of baked potatoes, and a quiet corner. I could just sit for days and nibble, that's all I want," Roman smacked his lips.

"We will erect grave stones for all our family at the old cemetery in Piotrkow, won't we, Roman, we must do that the first thing after this is all over, won't we?"

"We might, little brother, we might do that."

"But I am afraid too, Roman . . . I think I have forgotten what it means to be free."

"Don't worry, little brother, you will learn it all over again when the time comes."

We prayed fervently and we invoked the aid of the shadows.

"Remember us, O God, as You remember the children

247

that fell victims to the powers of iniquity. As You remember the desecrated parchments of the Torah and all those who died to sanctify Your name. Remember us, as You remember the shadows which hover eternally under the sky of the ghettos, remember us, and give us life, we pray."

And while we prayed for life, the enemy was preparing the camp for a final migration. The western Allies advanced from the south, and the Soviets approached from the east. SS reinforcements were brought in, and we received news of the forthcoming evacuation.

"Teresienstadt!"

The name of the dreaded camp in Czechoslovakia was on everybody's lips.

"But why? Why would they want to drag us down there so near the end? They'd make a faster retreat without six hundred marching corpses to watch!"

Scharführer Emil Tulka was in charge of the Kolditz operations. This was *his* domain. It was his to the very last, and he relished every moment of his unlimited authority.

"You understand, orders are orders. I don't mind telling you how much I dislike doing it, but orders from the Reichs-führer are very explicit. We move out tomorrow at dawn. We march for your own safety, the Soviets are close, some-day you will thank me for all this!"

Tulka spoke with a high-pitched, unpleasant voice. He was a veteran of the eastern front and bore two vivid remind-ers of that unsuccessful campaign, both bestowed upon him by his Vaterland—a glass eye and the Ritterkreuz II. Klasse.

"He sounds almost sincere."

"The world is full of sincere men, all ready to kill in the name of *their* sincerity."

"What do we do, Roman? What do we do?"

"One thing is clear, we're not going with them. We'll never make it. We are too close to the end to give up simply because Scharführer Tulka thinks it's best for us!"

We had no time for involved planning and that night, listening to the distant rumble of heavy artillery, we made our bid for freedom. It was relatively easy. We climbed onto the most elevated place in the large inactive factory furnace, a niche leading onto the tall chimney. Moments later our eyes adjusted to the complete darkness and our touch detected items we could not see.

"We'll sit tight till after they've gone," Roman theorized, "it's that simple."

We prayed. It was most likely the longest night we had ever experienced. Morning was announced by the shouting in the Appellplatz. We could distinguish the shrill voice of Scharführer Tulka, but dared not speak for fear we might be overheard. Several times during the morning the small metal shutter opened and closed, and the metallic sound reverberated through the hollow shell of our hideout. Each time it opened, our prayers increased.

We could only guess but it seemed to be late afternoon when the shouting stopped as suddenly as it had begun.

"Thank God, they're gone."

"We're safe," I whispered, "aren't we?"

"God only knows, be still, it might not be over yet."

"Eh, bambini!" a voice called out in Italian (the language of love), "we are here! Where are you? Say something, esta bene, it's fine, we're friends, where are you?"

We could not risk responding, and knowing that we shared our concealment made us realize that we were not the only escapees. "God, we would surely be missed!" I thought to myself. "Scharführer Tulka is nobody's fool; they'll search and find us. Even the Italians found it to be a good hiding place! We must leave, if we can, as soon as we can."

We spent hours in planning, and then, it was too late. Once again we heard the voice of Scharführer Tulka, but this time he spoke into the furnace:

"*Ist jemand hier?* Raus mit euch, verfluchte Schweine!

Raus mit euch *sofort, sonst machen wir Feuer!*" "Come out at once, or we'll fire the furnace!"

We hesitated and the SS forced one straw sack into the opening as a feeler. Tulka was about to light it when the two Italians emerged and fell to their knees.

"Please, let us live, there are four little ones and my wife waiting for me in Napoli, please, I meant no harm, I want to live," the one pleaded.

"Can you hear the big guns? The Americani are near, let us live! We are not fighters! Let us go to our families!"

"Is anyone else in there?" Tulka shouted, "tell the truth, is anyone hidden there beside you? Tell me and go free!"

The promise of life was generously offered and it took only a short moment for the Italians to make up their minds. Tulka placed his head once again into the opening. From our elevation we could see the glass eye in the narrow streak of light.

"Raus! Schweinehunde! Sofort raus!"

There was nothing we could do now but accept the blows as we surrendered. Tulka was enraged. The battle noises were closer and he was losing time.

"Marsch!" he shouted. The Italians attempted to apologize, the SS swore, and some of the young recruits laughed as they led us toward the center factory yard. It did not matter now. We prayed.

There were others lined up against the wall at the far end of the yard, their arms raised high.

"A miracle, Gotenyu, dear God, give us a miracle, please let us live!" The world was suddenly more beautiful than ever. It was a splendid April. The birds were chirping and the sun and clouds were painfully new.

"Dear God, we haven't yet begun to live . . . don't take us away yet . . . let us live dear God . . ."

Tulka ordered the machine gun trained on the line-up. "Feuer!"

Our prayers were almost as rapid as the gunfire. It all took only a few seconds and then the firing ceased.

"Thank you God. Praised be God. We are alive!"

Slowly we looked around. The two Italians were also alive since they too were last on the firing line. More than thirty men lay sprawled in puddles of blood.

"Begraben! Schnell!"

From the terse order, we understood we were to bury the dead as quickly as possible to conceal the evidence from the approaching Allies. We went about our work eagerly, still hoping to be spared.

As the last grave was dug, Tulka approached our work party, a submachine gun hanging from his shoulder. He smiled and his glass eye seemed almost real.

"You must dig much wider, we will need more space," he said and continued to smile.

"Let's say the Kaddish, Wilek, there will be no one left to say it for us."

"You must pray to me now," Tulka spoke and the smile disappeared from his glass eye. "You must worship me because your God is weak but I am here and I am the master. Pray to me and I will give you life."

We continued the Hebrew liturgy and hoped God would strike the blasphemer dead. Nothing happened and we dug the grave to the intended measurements.

"Stop! That's enough! Now, I ask you once again, will you pray to your true God? Will you pray to me?"

The Italians moved away from us and he pointed the gun at Roman.

"You! Get inside!"

Roman stepped down into the grave. We could hear the rattle of machine guns. The front was closing in.

"Please God, not now, not this near to life!"

Tulka fired and Roman fell with a narrow streak of blood running down the side of his mouth.

"Please let me speak to him, he is still alive! He is my brother, let me say a few words."

"Get inside and talk all you wish!"

Frantically I tried to keep Roman alive. I spoke tender words, loving words, and caressed his head in my arms. The second salvo sounded and the lights dimmed. The shadows whispered.

"Where are you . . . Roman . . . Srulko Malpo . . . Menasha . . . wait . . . Menasha."

And it came to pass . . .

A New World has sprung from the ashes
Of its own devastation. And Balder did
Return from the bonds of Hel, to live
Among the good and righteous men . . .

And order came, Chaos was no more . . .

And Life was born out of the Death.
And Good once more defeated Evil.
But Loki did escape, alone, into the
Sinister mysteries of Hel . . .

And the sages wait in fear . . .

For Loki vowed his wrath to keep,
Lest in his scorn he, once again,
Will show his ugly head, and fight,
Until the bitter End will come with RAGNARÖK. . . .

APPENDIX

I. SONGS OF THE GHETTO
II. GLOSSARY OF FOREIGN TERMS

I. Songs Of The Ghetto

VOO AH-HEEN ZOL EEKH GAYN . . . ? (YIDDISH VERSION)

Voo ah-heen zol eekh gayn . . . ?
Ahz yeh-dehr teer eez fahr-makht.
Voo ah-heen zol eekh gayn?
Ahz ee-behr-ahl shtayt dee vakt.

Voo ah-heen zol eekh gayn?
Hayst men meer blye-ben shtayn
Voo ah-heen zol eekh gayn?
Zogt men meer "yood blibe shtayn."
Hash-kee-vay-noo nah-zahd.

O BUCHENWALD (GERMAN VERSION)

Wenn der Tag erwacht,
eh' die Sonne lacht,
die Kolonnen zieh'n
zu des Tages Müh'n
hinein in den grauenden Morgen.
Und der Wald ist schwarz und der Himmel rot,
und wir tragen im Brotsack ein Stückchen Brot
und im Herzen, im Herzen die Sorgen.
  O Buchenwald, ich kann dich nicht vergessen,
  weil du mein Schicksal bist!
  Wer dich verliess, der kann es erst ermessen,
  wie wundervoll die Freiheit ist.
  O Buchenwald, wir jammern nicht und klagen,
  und was auch unser Schicksal sei:
  Wir wollen trotzdem Ja zum Leben sagen,
  denn einmal kommt der Tag, dann sind wir frei!

Wir wollen Ja zum Leben sagen,
  denn einmal kommt der Tag, dann sind wir frei.
Und die Nacht ist heiss,
Und das Mädel fern,
und der Wind singt leis',
und ich hab' sie so gern,
wenn treu sie, ja treu sie nur bliebe!
Und die Steine sind hart, aber fest unser Schritt,
und wir tragen die Picken und Spaten mit
und im Herzen, im Herzen die Liebe.
  O Buchenwald . . . (Refrain)
Doch die Nacht ist kurz,
und der Tag ist so lang—
Und ein Lied erklingt,
das die Heimat sang:
Wir lassen den Mut uns nicht rauben!
Halte Schritt, Kamerad, und verlier' nicht den Mut,

denn wir tragen den Willen zum leben im Blut
und im Herzen, im Herzen den Glauben!
O Buchenwald . . .

II. Glossary of Foreign Terms

ABBREVIATIONS: (F) French (G) German (H) Hebrew
(I) Italian (L) Latin (P) Polish
(R) Russian (Y) Yiddish (ON) Old Norse

al Kiddush hashem (H)	died for the sanctification of His Name
also (G)	then, now then
Appell (G)	rollcall
Appellplatz (G)	assembly yard
Arbeitslager (G)	labor camp
arme Teufel (G)	poor devils
Armja Krajowa—A.K. (P)	the resistance movement consisting of rightist elements; freely translated—Home Army
Bar Mitzvah (H)	confirmation of a thirteen-year-old boy into manhood
Bekanntmachung (G)	announcement
begraben (G)	bury
bleib stehen (G)	stand still
bliższe ciało niż koszula (P)	the skin is closer than the shirt
Blockälteste (G)	the barrack cadre
Brigadeführer (G)	SS rank equal to Maj. General (literally "brigade leader")
B'rith Mila (H)	the ceremony of circumcision
Bruderschaft (G)	brotherhood
brudny żydzie (P)	dirty Jew
co czerwone to piekne (P)	beautiful things come in red
Cohanim (H)	priests
dayenu (H)	enough

der Alte wird uns helfen (G)	the Old Man will help us
der Grosse (G)	the Great one
der wird dich (G)	he will . . . you
Deutschland über alles (G)	Germany above all else (German national anthem)
din Torah (H)	litigation
droshke (Y)	a horse-drawn taxi
Eisenbahnstr. (G)	Railroad street
Entlausungshaus (G)	delousing house
Entlausungsraum (G)	delousing area
euch (G)	you
Feuer (G)	fire
Gabah (Y)	the keeper of the temple
Ganev (Y)	thief
Gauleiter (G)	District Governor
Gefreiter (G)	Private First Class (Pfc.), lance corporal
geh' mit ihm (G)	go with him
Gemara (H)	Discussion of Jewish Law, based on the Mishnah; both together constitute the Talmud
Golem (Y)	idiot, factotum
Goluth (H)	exile
goy (Y)	gentile
Gruppenführer (G)	SS rank, equivalent to Lt. General (literally "group leader")
haham (H)	literally "wise one," also rabbi
Halt, wer kommt da! (G)	Halt, who goes there!
Haskalah (H)	reform assimilation movement
HJ—Hitler-Jugend (G)	Hitler Youth
Hasid (H)	orthodox Jew (literally "follower of the Rabbi")
Hausbursche (G)	orderly
Heder (Y)	Hebrew religious school
Heimwehr (G)	home guard
herein (G)	enter
Herrenvolk (G)	master race

Hevrah Kadishah (H)	holy burial society
hozon (H)	cantor
Humash (H)	literally "a fifth," i.e. the Pentateuch
Hund (G)	dog
ich melde gehorsam (G)	I report respectfully
ist jemand hier? (G)	is someone there?
Jawohl (G)	yes, Sir
Judenfrage (G)	the Jewish question
Judenfrei (G)	without Jews
Judenrat (G)	Jewish Council
Judenstadt (G)	Jewish city
Judenreinigung (G)	liquidation of Jews
Jude verrecke! (G)	Jew, die!
Jugend (G)	youth
Kaddish (H)	mourner's prayer
Keren Kayemet L'Israel (H)	Jewish National Fund
Kiddush (H)	sanctification of wine on Sabbath
Khorosho (R)	good, well
Knochenmühle (G)	bone-grinder
komm' (G)	come
Kommandantur (G)	Command headquarters
Koved (H)	Prestige, glory; respect
Kriegsgefangene (G)	Prisoners of war
Kultur (G)	culture
Kulturverwalter (G)	cultural administrator
Kunst (G)	art
Lagerkommandant (G)	Camp Commandant
Lebensraum (G)	living space
le boche s'en va (F)	the German flees
leiten (G)	lead, take
Liebchen (G)	dear one, darling
Maarev	afternoon prayers
Makher (Y)	wheeler dealer
Malpo (Y)	monkey
Mamzehr (Y)	a product of adultery or incest

Maskil (H)	person interested in secular pursuits and in critical study of Judaism, departing from strict Talmudic framework
Mazal tov (H)	good luck
meine Herren (G)	gentlemen
Mein Kampf (G)	book by Adolf Hitler, literally "My Struggle"
Melammed (H)	teacher
Mikvah (Y)	ritual bath
minyan (H)	a quorum of ten men over 13 years of age constituting a congregation for public worship
Mischling ersten Grades (G)	literally hybrid of first degree, "half-Jew"
Mischling zweiten Grades (G)	literally hybrid of second degree, "quarter-Jew"
Mishna (H)	Code of Jewish Law
Muttersprache (G)	mother tongue
nachas (H)	a deep, quiet joy in the achievements of one's children
NSDAP (G)	National Socialist German Workers Party
Oberschlesier (G)	from Upper Silesia
Obersturmbannführer (G)	SS rank equal to Lt. Colonel
O Tannenbaum, O Tannenbaum, wie treu sind deine Blätter (G)	Christmas song—Oh Christmas Tree, Oh Christmas Tree, how faithful are your leaves
Panzerfaust (G)	bazooka
Panzergruppe (G)	Armored Group
Polizeiausweis (G)	Police identification papers
Praeceptor Germaniae (L)	the Leader of Germany
pünktlich (G)	exactly, on time
Ragnarök (ON)	Twilight of the Gods
Raus, zum Appell (G)	out, for rollcall
Realgymnasium (G)	secondary school with scientific bias
Recht (G)	right